YOGA LIFE

A Workbook of Authentic Practices

Caroline McCarter

Illustrations by Robert Wymer

Printed in the United States of America.

ISBN 978-0-692-13146-6

This book is dedicated to my students and clients, who teach me every day how to be a better person. I am deeply indebted to you for every moment I get to be with you.

This project wouldn't exist if not for the skill and finesse of Patty Moynahan. Not just an editor, she was a light in the dark whenever I felt stuck or scared. "Just keep moving those rocks!"

Thank you to Jim Grubbs and the Uncommon Health Initiatives Foundation, for giving me hope right from the start, and to David Hurwitz, for guidance at the finish line. Finally, I offer thanks to my teachers A.G., Indra, and Ganesh Mohan.

Table of Contents

INTRODUCTION

My introduction to Yoga was through a VHS tape my mother handed to me when I was a teenager. Like most teens I was skeptical and aloof, so the tape sat gathering dust, until I became nostalgic for my days as a gymnast. I began watching the tape. I started breathing and moving according to the instructions. Some of the moves were so simple I didn't understand why anyone would need a video for them. But halfway through the video, the instructor proposed holding a downward dog posture for five minutes with deep breathing. I came to my knees, lightheaded, shortly after 30 seconds in the pose. I had no idea breathing could be so difficult.

I practiced with that Yoga video and several others until I finally made it to my first Yoga class at the University of Michigan. There I discovered aspects of Yoga beyond simply moving the body with breath. Our professor introduced us to specific breathing and mental focus techniques—meditation—while teaching us archaic philosophical principles in Sanskrit. I was confused and enamored all at once. How could these fitness techniques help me feel less stressed by my school schedule and job? How could they help me with the general malaise I felt about life?

My life proceeded quickly with many changes—my degree, marriage, a professional job, graduate school, and a cross-country move. Throughout all of this I was steadfast in my home practice of Yoga. In my late 20s I finally took my first group class, and not long after that, Yoga teacher training.

I trained about 10 years after my mother gave me that tape. At that time, group Yoga classes were becoming more popular, and I wanted to see what the hubbub was about. After taking a few classes, I discovered that I didn't enjoy them very much, for the following reasons:

1. I felt claustrophobic with so many people and mats packed into a small room.
2. I became distracted with competitive thoughts, trying to be the best in the room.
3. Many classes focused on perfection, which seemed superficial to me.
4. There was no breath work, meditation, or discussion about how to find peace outside of your practice.

As my studies deepened, I found more solace practicing in private, where I could move freely, read and contemplate concepts, and not have my body as the sole object of my focus. When I studied to be a teacher, I was always thinking about how I could encourage people to experience Yoga in a different way—not in a group, one-size-fits-all class, but in a setting that would promote a deeper sense of quietude and personal health, using practices tailored uniquely to individual students.

It was that curiosity that sent me to India for the first time to study with the Mohan family—A.G., Indra, and Ganesh. They were offering personal integration practices and Yoga therapy practices that were solely about an individual's needs, rather than those of a group. It was also notable they had studied with Tirumalai Krishnamacharya (1888-1989) who is still one of the most renowned teachers of Yoga. In the Mohan home I came to a deeper understanding of Yoga, of how to use it for my own path of peace, and of how to share it with others in a true and authentic way.

In 2006 I created my private Yoga therapy practice in Austin, Texas. The idea of writing this book came from clients. While many came to me for relief of physical ailments, they were also interested in controlling their anger, frustration, stress, depression, and more. If you drop in on any of my classes, on any given day, you will hear me explaining that the objective of Yoga is to create more peace of mind through direction of thoughts. Clients began asking me, "Where can I get a book on what you're talking about?" There are many Yoga books, including books about the *Yoga Sutras*. But most books about the Yoga Sūtras are only for those who are experienced. They are Yoga adepts. I'm writing for everyone, and so I have created this book.

Is this book for you?

- The answer is yes if you:
- have no experience of Yoga but have heard of its benefits
- have limited experience of Yoga and want to know more
- are familiar with Yoga but haven't delved into its philosophy
- notice the peaceful feeling acquired in class disappears as soon as you resume daily life
- are a Yoga adept but have an interest in exploring differing experiences and opinions
- are a teacher in training and want to expand your knowledge of Yoga
- are a Yoga therapist hoping to help your clients with specific take-home exercises
- are curious about your thoughts and patterns of behavior

How to use this book

This is a workbook that invites your participation. At first you may have reservations about doing the exercises and may simply want to read through the book. That's absolutely reasonable. Many of you will want to plunge right in, reading and doing all the exercises as you go. Or, you may want to pick and choose certain exercises that grab your attention. My preference would be that you move through the text in order, as I have placed introductory topics that are helpful for later exercises. But this is not required. The most important purpose of this book is to help you to engage in looking at your mind, your "self," and your thoughts, and to explore what reflections and changes could be made using Yoga.

What you will need

You will likely need an extra journal for some of the writing exercises. I recommend getting a pen or pencil that feels just right in your hand, as well as a journal that is solely for the journey you are about to take. Keep in mind, though: There is no right way or wrong way to participate in the assignments.

A note on Sanskrit terms

I have included some Sanskrit terms in this book. Knowing Sanskrit is not required, but becoming familiar with some aspects of it can be helpful. There are many words in Sanskrit that don't have a simple one-word, literal English translation. Throughout the book I may use several English terms to help you understand one concept in *Sanskrit.*

To make it easier for you, all *Sanskrit* terms that I use are listed in italics and have a pronunciation guide in the Glossary on pg. xx. There's no need to pronounce these terms perfectly to use this book. I've just added this information for those of you interested in languages, or in Sanskrit specifically.

Movement Diagrams

There are worded instructions as well as stick-figure diagrams to make the movement practices clear. There are also arrows to direct the breath, which signify an "IN" for inhale and "EX" for exhale.

Guidance

No matter how you use this book, my intention is for it to be of help to you. Some of you may want to use it in a book group; some of you may want to do the exercises with a close friend or teacher; others of you may want to work through the book on your own.

I have put years of personal studies and years of teaching into this workbook. Many of the activities are ones that have proven helpful to clients on their individual paths. No matter what your reason for reading and using this workbook, I'm guessing that you and I share at least one common interest: the desire for more peace of mind in our lives.

Thank you, and peace be with you.

PART 1

WELCOME TO YOUR MIND

The definitive text on Yoga, the *Yoga Sūtras of Patanjali*, is thought to have been written more than 2,500 years ago. Little is known about Patanjali (puh•TAHN•juh•lee), but he appears in various myths and legends that celebrate his timeless knowledge. Patanjali's work contains 195 concise statements, or *sūtras*, that address the systematic process of attaining self-knowledge and, ultimately, the state of absolute freedom. The definition of Yoga is stated in the Yoga *Sūtras*:

yoga citta vṛtti nirodha

An English equivalent of yoga *citta vṛtti nirodha* would be "Yoga is the ability to direct the thoughts of the mind." The *Yoga Sūtras* are absolutely clear: the aim of a Yoga practice is to move toward *citta vṛtti nirodha*, a focused and peaceful mind.

Why so much focus on the mind? *I thought the practice of Yoga was about the body?*

This is a question I'm often asked. In the Western world, the focus of many Yoga classes is on the body—on improving flexibility and physical strength. But those are *byproducts of Yoga*, not the goal. Yoga was developed to address the nature of the mind, which is often the source of unwise behaviors and unhappiness if we don't understand its nature.

Part 1 invites readers to explore the *nature* of the mind by using Yoga to look deeply at the function of the mind. This calls for mindfulness. In the last several decades, mindfulness practices have been the subjects of books, news articles, and scientific studies—particularly as techniques for reducing stress. Mindfulness is inherent in Yoga. It is the practice of cultivating awareness of how our mind functions.

Yogic mindfulness can help us:

- understand the link between our thoughts and our behaviors
- recognize alternative ways of thinking and behaving
- broaden our perspective
- maintain a clear focus
- appreciate the richness of each moment

CHAPTER

1

The Mind's Job

The mind's job is to generate thoughts. In this chapter we will explore the yogic understanding of how thoughts arise. We will also examine familiar cycles, or patterns, of thought.

Throughout our exploration, let's be compassionate, rather than critical, toward our mind. Even when our mind baffles and frustrates us, it's only doing its job.

Let's return to the definition of Yoga from *Patanjali's Yoga Sūtras*:

yoga citta vṛtti nirodha

Yoga is the ability to direct our thoughts. Yoga is this ability, and Yoga *cultivates* this ability.

Why is it important to direct our thoughts? The mind can be like a two-year-old: easily distracted and prone to wander into trouble unknowingly! The ancient Yoga sages understood that our *thoughts*, rather than external events, cause our unhappiness. If we cannot direct our thoughts, we become directed *by* them and by the impulses they generate. Sometimes this is not a bad thing, but often it's the source of our discontent.

Through Yoga, we develop the ability to understand and direct our thoughts so that when situations arise that have the potential to create unhappiness in us, we can move into a more neutral, peaceful, or even transcendent place. When we consciously direct our thoughts, we become clearer about our motives and act in ways that promote peace and well-being.

A yogic mind is a mind without conflict.

1.1.1

If you have a current Yoga practice, take a moment to answer the questions below. Write your answers in the space provided, or in your journal.

- Does your Yoga practice inspire a feeling of peacefulness? Explain your answer.

____

____

____

- What do you notice about your state of mind *during* your Yoga practice?

____

____

____

Continued on next page

Continued

1.1.1

- What do you notice about your state of mind *after* your Yoga practice?

____

____

____

- How do you define the concept "peace of mind"?______________________

____

____

____

The mind's purpose is solely to think.

This understanding of the mind's job is of utmost importance on the yogic path. It is the foundation of all aspects of the practice.

Vṛtti is frequently translated as "activities." But the literal translation from Sanskrit to English is "profession or job." This translation is more to the point: the relentless flow of thoughts sustains the mind, just as our jobs help sustain our lives.

Let's observe our mind just doing its job.

1.1.2

Find a quiet place to sit, free of interruptions. Seat yourself in a comfortable position. Then set a timer for two minutes. Simply observe the movement of your thoughts for two minutes. Then write about your observations.

- What did you notice during the exercise? ______________________

____

____

- Would you rate your mental activity as fast, medium, or slow?

____

____

- What patterns, if any, did you notice in your thinking? ______________________

____

____

- Did the same thoughts keep returning, or were the thoughts varied?

____

____

____

Trying to stop the mind from thinking is futile. We may as well ask our liver or heart to stop doing its job. Therefore, to scold our mind for producing thoughts is useless. The mind is just doing what it does. But because we so easily *identify* with our thoughts, we end up scolding ourselves for our thinking. If we criticize or fight with our mind, we may make things worse for ourselves. In the next two exercises, we'll explore ways in which we attack ourselves for our thinking.

Note: Do not scold your mind for wandering during the next two exercises, or any other exercise in this workbook. Just gently escort the mind back to the exercise, again and again.

1.1.3

Think of times you've criticized yourself for your thinking, or fought with your mind.

- Describe a recent situation in which you found yourself criticizing, arguing with, or fighting with your mind.

  ____

  ____

- If you fully understood that *the mind's job is to generate thoughts*, how might this understanding change your point of view and behavior?

  ____

  ____

Let's explore rerouting our minds as a parent might reroute a child's behavior. If you have children, you've probably perfected the art of distraction, which can sometimes be more effective than scolding your child. In this next exercise, we'll explore ways to *distract* rather than *scold* ourselves for our thinking.

1.1.4

Just for today, notice moments when you scold yourself, even mildly. Then write about one of these moments. Describe the situation in which your scolding occurred, the thought you had, and how you could have distracted (or did distract) yourself from dwelling on the thought. Examples are in parentheses.

- Situation (*asking my boss for a raise*): ______________________________

  ____

  ____

- Thought (*I don't deserve a raise.*): ______________________________

  ____

  ____

- Helpful Distraction (*focusing on my boss's demeanor and words; concentrating on my breath*): ______________________________

  ____

The practice of Yoga leads us to peaceful stillness. Imagine a pond in which the water is calm. If we touch the water, we create a ripple that expands. We have, in a sense, disturbed the calm state of the pond. But the pond is within a "container" of land, which will eventually absorb the ripples and return the pond to stillness.

Our mind is like this pond, and our thoughts are like the ripples. Yoga—the "container" for our fluctuating thoughts—returns us to stillness.

Think about ways you might restore calmness and stillness to your mind. Perhaps you take walks, sip a cup of tea, or play the piano. These methods are *citta vṛtti nirodha*. In other words, they are Yoga.

1.1.5

What are some ways that you are *already* practicing Yoga, in the sense of deliberately bringing calmness, steadiness, and peacefulness to your mind? Perform one of these calming activities today—even if your mind is not disturbed—and make notes about your state of mind and feelings before and after the activity.

- Calming activity: ____________________

- State of mind and feelings *before* the activity:

- State of mind and feelings *after* the activity:

Cycles of guilt. Let's return to those moments in which we react negatively to our thoughts. You've heard the saying "Love makes the world go 'round." I have heard it said that it's actually guilt that makes the world go 'round.

An effective way to disturb our mind is to entertain a guilty thought and then follow it with self-recrimination. *Why did I say such a thoughtless thing? . . . I should've called my friend on his birthday . . . I shouldn't have eaten that second piece of cake . . .* We create little "perfect storms" for ourselves in this way. The negative thoughts fuel more guilt, which triggers more self-criticism that makes us feel badly enough to eat a *third* piece of cake.

Notice the ways in which you criticize yourself—notice especially the words and the *tone* of these criticisms. Would you speak this way to your best friend? Just for one day, pay attention to your critical self-talk.

1.1.6

For today, do not try to change your critical self-talk. Just observe it as a scientist might. Write down some of the criticisms and describe their tone. Then write a kinder, gentler way of stating the criticisms (if they are warranted). Some examples are in parentheses.

- What was the self-criticism? (*I can't believe I forgot my dentist appointment. I'm such a dunce!*) ______________________________

  ____

  ____

- What was the tone of your criticism? (*authoritative and shaming*) ______________________________

  ____

  ____

- What is a kinder alternative? (*I've had a lot on my mind lately, and we all forget things sometimes. I'll reschedule that appointment now.*) ______________________________

  ____

  ____

  ____

We can experiment with calming ourselves during a "perfect storm." In the next exercise, we'll notice the effects of taking a breath, holding it, and releasing it. There is no "best way" to do the exercise. We're simply noticing what we feel and think during the exercise. Read the instructions and memorize them before beginning, since the exercise is meant to be done with the eyes closed. Alternatively, you can ask a friend or partner to read the instructions aloud.

1.1.7

Find a quiet space in which you will be free from interruption. When you finish the exercise, make notes of your thoughts and feelings.

1. Take a seated position in a chair or on a cushion. Sit with a straight, but not rigid, back. You want to be comfortable.
2. Lower your chin slightly and close your eyes.
3. Inhale deeply, filling your whole torso.
4. Hold the inhale for a count of 5.
5. Exhale.
6. Repeat for a total of 5 breaths.

Continued on next page

Continued

1.1.7

- Feelings/thoughts during my first inhale/exhale: ____

____

____

- Feelings/thoughts during my last inhale/exhale:____

____

____

The next two exercises are designed to sharpen our awareness of what is *outside* our mind, waiting to be discovered in every moment. These exercises offer a way to help us engage with what's available when we're not preoccupied with our opinions, preferences, defenses, emotions, fantasies, and plans.

1.1.8

Before you go to sleep tonight, set an intention to not hurry out of bed tomorrow morning. Plan to wake up about 10–15 minutes earlier than usual, and have this workbook nearby. When you awaken, remain still and quiet enough to almost hear your heartbeat. Place your hand over your heart. Sharpen *all* of your senses and notice what you see, hear, smell, taste, and feel. Then slowly and quietly leave your bed and write about the experience.

- What I saw: ____

____

- What I heard: ____

____

____

- What I smelled: ____

____

____

- What I tasted: ____

____

____

- What I felt (through touch): ____

____

____

- What was pleasant/unpleasant about the experience:____

____

____

What we have. In our next exercise we will become aware of how easy it is to be preoccupied with what we *lack*, rather than what we already *have*. Television, magazines, movies, and the Internet aggressively remind us of what we lack and *must have* in order to be happy and fulfilled. Sooner or later, though, events can remind us how fortunate we are—even if, according to our culture's materialistic standards, we lack many things.

1.1.9

Choose one day this week to imagine that everything you encounter is a precious gift. Live as though you'd suddenly awakened to life's true richness. Resist the urge to become irritated by the behavior of your partner, friend, or coworker. Seek loveliness in those around you. At the end of the day, write about your experiences. Note at least three things for which you're grateful.

- What I noticed about myself, about others, and about my surroundings: ____________________

____

____

____

____

- What do you notice about your state of mind during your Yoga practice? ____________________

____

____

____

____

"The moment one give close attention to anything, even a blade of grass, it becomes a mysterious, awesome, indescribably magnificent world in itself."

~Henry Miller

2 Thoughtlessness and Thoughtfulness

In this chapter we'll further explore our powers of observation. *Thoughtfulness*, in the sense of *mindfulness or attentiveness*, means taking ourselves off "automatic pilot" and being present in all that we do.

Thoughtfulness takes practice because many of our everyday actions are *thoughtless*, in the sense that we do them automatically—brushing our teeth, putting on our shoes, getting a glass of water, eating a meal, even driving a car. We also obey impulses thoughtlessly that arise from thoughts, such as the impulse to lash out at the driver who veers into our lane or the impulse to eat because we're bored.

"The world is too much with us," begins William Wordsworth's famous poem. Many forces compete for our attention—email, texts, voicemails, television, talk radio, billboard ads, YouTube. So much "noise" assaults us that it seems normal—until it stops and we realize how intrusive it has become. The next exercise can remind us of how much we hear—or fail to hear—in each moment.

1.2.1

Close your eyes and try to identify sounds far from you—sounds outside the room and outside the house or building where you are.

- Sounds far from me: ____________________

____

____

____

Next, close your eyes and listen for sounds in the room where you are.

- Sounds near me: ____________________

____

____

____

Now close your eyes and listen for sounds within your body.

- Sounds within my body: ____________________

____

____

____

- What did you notice about the experience of such deep listening? ____________________

____

____

____

Not all sounds lead to unwanted distractions. Many sounds can soothe us. We can practice thoughtful listening by seeking sounds that calm us.

1.2.2

Think of sounds that you associate with peacefulness, from your childhood to the present, such as surf breaking on the shore, leaves being stirred by a breeze, or a father singing a lullaby.

List the sounds below.

____

____

____

____

For one or two minutes, sit quietly and recall a sound that you listed. Let the sound come fully into your mind. When it recedes, gently bring it back. Write about the experience.

____

____

____

____

Let's return to an exercise that promotes thoughtful breathing.

1.2.3

Sit in a chair in a room with no distractions. Straighten your back, and lower your chin slightly. Take 2–3 relaxed breaths. Then begin the exercise.

1. Inhale slowly. Feel the lower ribcage expand and the breath move upward in the chest.
2. Exhale slowly, drawing the abdomen in and upward throughout the exhale.
3. Repeat steps 1 and 2 for at least ten inhale/exhale cycles.

What I observed during the exercise: ______________________________

____

____

____

____

____

____

____

***Ujjayi* breathing.** In Yoga we often use *ujjayi* breathing, in which you gently constrict the throat so that you have a clearer sense of the breath coming in and going out. To get a sense of *ujjayi* breathing, first whisper the word *hah* on a long exhale, as if you were fogging a mirror. Now do this again, with the lips closed. You should feel a soft rubbing sensation in the throat and hear a sound like a sigh. Now try *ujjayi* breathing on an inhale.

Ujjayi breathing may feel strange at first, but with practice it becomes very natural. It is meant to be done only during certain focused Yoga practices. Let's try it in an exercise.

1.2.4

Sit in a chair in a room with no distractions. Straighten your back. Lower your chin slightly. Take 2–3 relaxed breaths. Then begin the exercise. Use *ujjayi* breathing on the inhale/exhale cycles. Afterward, note your observations. Try to do this exercise two more times during the day.

1. Inhale slowly and mentally say "one"; exhale slowly and mentally say "one."

2. Inhale slowly and mentally say "two"; exhale slowly and mentally say "two."

3. Repeat for at least ten inhale/exhale cycles, or for about 3 minutes.

What I observed during the exercise: ______________________________

____

____

____

____

____

____

Breath and movement. In Yoga, we add slow, thoughtful movement to our *ujjayi* breathing to reach a deeper level of awareness and calmness.
The breath is an "envelope" that contains the movement. This means that the movement does not begin until just *after* an inhale or exhale has begun. The movement stops *before* the inhale or exhale is complete.

In the next exercise, try to maintain a sense of the posture suggested below as occurring *inside* your breath. It may take a few tries to coordinate breath and movement. This should feel comfortable and fluid. If you find yourself running out of breath, stop and take a couple of easy breaths without movement before trying the exercise again.

1.2.5

EXERCISE 1.2.5

Stand with your back straight but not rigid. Rest your arms at your sides. Alternatively, sit in a chair that allows you to straighten your back. Use *ujjayi* breathing, if you can do so comfortably in this exercise. After the exercise, note your observations.

❶ Begin inhaling slowly. After a second or two, slowly begin raising your arms forward and up, doing so as you continue to inhale. Raise the arms as high as they will comfortably extend, and then allow the inhale to finish.

❷ Begin exhaling slowly, drawing the abdomen in and upward. After a second or two, slowly begin lowering your arms throughout the exhale. Finish the movement just before the exhale ends.

❸ Take two or three easy breaths. Then repeat steps 1 and 2, twice more, for a total of three arm raises. (Include step 3, if you are feeling short of breath.)

What I observed during the exercise:

____

____

____

____

____

____

EXERCISE 1.2.5

1.2.5

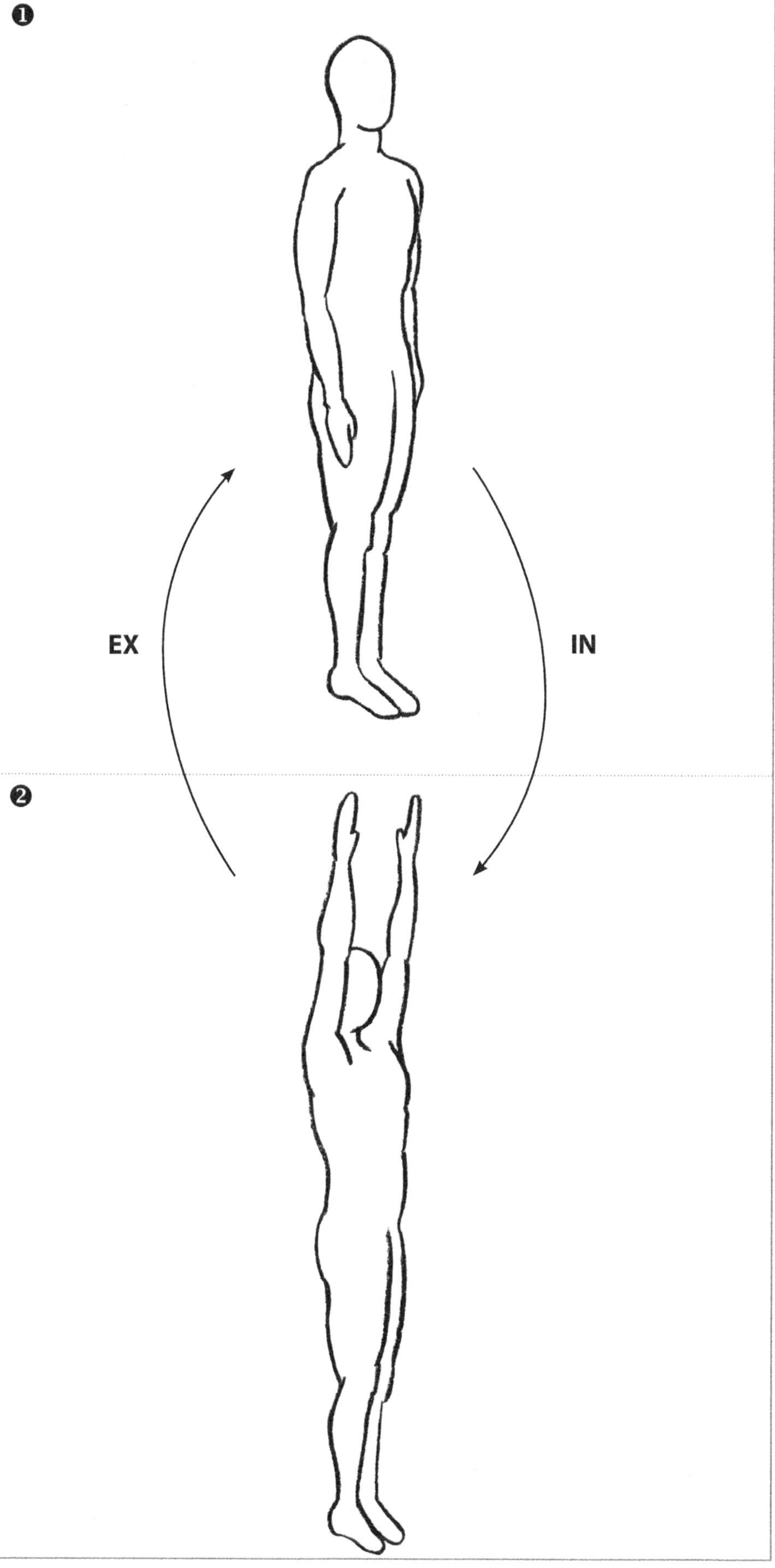

Few of our daily activities are performed as deliberately as we performed the arm raises. During the exercise did you notice your mind feeling clearer, or perhaps you were less distracted by your thoughts? This simple practice can reveal the wonder—and even the joy—of uniting breath and body to bring about peace of mind. When you feel frazzled during the day, you can use this exercise to return to your true "home," a place of stillness and peace.

Thoughtful action. It's easy to be driven by an impulsive thought, which leads to a behavior in which unhappiness is the end result. The following example illustrates this:

Thought: *I see and smell French fries. I want some!*

Action: *I order the French fries and eat them.*

Result: *Ugh! Now I've got indigestion.*

One way to be thoughtful is to question our actions before we take them. To question our every action would be exhausting, but let's experiment with this type of thoughtfulness in the next exercise.

1.2.6 Choose a day, or part of a day, to observe your actions—such as deciding how to spend free moments, choosing what to eat for a meal, making a purchase, or reacting to an email. Recall your thinking process before, during, and after the action. Were the results satisfactory? Why or why not?

- One or more actions you observed: ______________________________

____

____

- Motivation(s) for the action(s): ______________________________

____

____

- Thoughts/feelings before taking the action(s): ______________________________

____

____

- Thoughts/feelings while taking the action(s): ______________________________

____

____

- Thoughts/feelings after taking the action(s): ______________________________

____

____

- Your assessment of the action(s) (e.g., satisfactory/unsatisfactory): ______________________________

____

____

Thoughtful speech. We have all spoken in anger or frustration and later regretted our words. Restraining our speech—especially when we're angry—is a basic practice in Yoga. It is a form of *ahimsā*, or refraining from doing harm, which we'll explore more deeply in Part 4.

Sometimes thoughtful speech means choosing our words and tone carefully, to be clear and to avoid causing harm. It can also mean saying very little, or nothing at all. Even if we cannot control our endless internal monologue, we *can* control the quality and quantity of our external speech.

1.2.7

Just for one day, or part of a day, be conservative with your speaking. Choose your words carefully—do not waste them. Honor others by not repeating yourself or chattering aimlessly or loudly. Treat the act of speaking as a sacred gift not to be squandered.

- Describe your observations after being conservative with speaking: ____________________

- What, if anything, was pleasant about the experience? ____________________

- What, if anything, was unpleasant about the experience?____________________

Choose part of a day, or an entire day, to refrain from speaking at all.

- Describe your observations after not speaking at all: ____________________

- What, if anything, was pleasant about the experience?____________________

- What, if anything, was unpleasant about the experience?____________________

Thoughtful eating. We're in a hurry—no time for a proper breakfast. We grab a protein bar and gobble it down on the way to work. We hardly notice the act of eating. Our attention is focused instead on steering the car and listening to the radio.

It's easy to forget how special it is to eat a meal—especially a meal with loved ones. One of the costs of frenzied living is losing the joy of a communal meal. This next exercise may be difficult. It is for me, at times, but forge ahead through the difficulty and give it a try.

1.2.8

Eat one meal this week in complete silence. This is easier if you eat alone, but it can be interesting with a partner or friend. Devote all of your attention to the act of eating—no television, music, computer, or reading matter allowed.
Eat with a sense of nourishing your soul, not just your body. Then write about the experience.

- What, if anything, was pleasant about the experience ______________________________
- What, if anything, was unpleasant about the experience?______________________________
- Other observations about thoughtful eating:______________________________

CHAPTER

3 Mind Games

Our mind can surprise and delight us. It can also baffle and frustrate us. Sometimes it's a magician, pulling unexpected rabbits out of a hat. Or a sage, producing bursts of wisdom like fireworks. It can be the uninvited guest that spoils the party with unfounded fears and angry accusations. Or it can be our sensible companion and guide.

Before I became a Yoga teacher I was a librarian, so it's easy for me to compare the mind to a library. We cannot comprehend the vastness of our mind's collection of stored memories, sensations, or experiences. There are uncountable rooms containing uncountable rows of shelves in the library of the mind.

As we continue to explore the nature of the mind, let's have some fun with a word-association exercise. This is like a game between our mind and our observing self.

1.3.1

For each word below, write the first word or image that comes to your mind. Don't think about your response; there's no trick or hidden meaning. No one else will see the results. Just move quickly through the exercise. When you have finished, review the list and note any surprising associations.

1. safety: ______________________
2. book: ______________________
3. chocolate: ______________________
4. garden: ______________________
5. desire: ______________________

Surprising associations: ______________________

____

____

____

____

____

____

____

The judging (and misjudging) mind. You're walking to your car one afternoon after a downtown meeting. Ahead on the sidewalk you see the rumpled figure of a man. He's leaning on a parking meter. You cautiously walk toward the man. He's mumbling. Then he slumps to the sidewalk. He lies on his back, gesturing and speaking nonsense.

"Oh, brother," you say to yourself. "It's only 4:30, and this man is completely drunk." You cross the street and keep walking. Then you hear a commotion. You turn to see a woman crouched near the man, talking to him. The woman sees you and yells. "Help! This man is a diabetic. He's in a crisis. I don't have my phone. Please—call an ambulance!"

You can't be blamed for mistaking a diabetic emergency for a case of drunkenness. But it's an example of how the mind uses prior experience (or lack thereof), beliefs, and prejudices to form judgments that can be seriously wrong.

It's hard for us to make an observation without a judgment. This is part of our survival instinct—*is this a rope or a snake? Friend or foe?* Even when we're not in a life-or-death situation, we turn observations into judgments, as in, "He didn't return my text today; he must not like me."

Yoga can help us gain clarity so that we're not so quick to jump from observation to judgment. The practice of Yoga teaches that we can choose which thoughts to attend to and which to ignore. This allows us to conserve our "judging energy" for times when it's really called for.

The next exercise can remind us of how our mind can mislead us. It begins with a familiar allegory.

1.3.2

A man is seated in a boat on a calm river. As he watches the last rays of the sun dissolve behind the distant mountains, he feels peaceful—and a bit lonely. A light fog has settled on the river's surface. Suddenly, he sees another boat coming toward him. "How nice!" he thinks to himself. "Now I will have someone to share this moment with." But then he notices that the boat is speeding toward him. The man yells, "Hey! Be careful there!" But the boat continues on its course. Now the man is in a panic. He leaps up and frantically waves his arms. He screams, "STOP!" just before the other boat crashes into his boat. The impact knocks the man off his feet. He manages to rise, still shaking all over. Then he notices that the boat that hit him was empty all along.

What does this story symbolize to you? Write about a situation in which you reacted as did the man in the story.

The comfort and fallacy of judging. Even when we're not misjudging a situation or person, the act of judging can create a disturbance for us. We often make judgments to comfort ourselves in the midst of uncertainty, forgetting that uncertainty is the normal human condition. We can never know for sure what will happen in the next moment or the moment after that. The options that could be our future are endless. This can make us feel like we have no control over our lives, which is potentially frightening. So we develop strategies that help us feel in control.

We make judgments—*this is good, that is not good; she is kind, he is unkind; this is helpful, that is not helpful.* We feel safe when we judge and categorize. But this sense of safety is not only fleeting but false. It separates us from reality, because reality is seldom black or white.

Let's explore our judging, categorizing, discriminating minds in the next exercise.

1.3.3

Do you ever use categories to judge persons, place, things, organizations, concepts, or traditions—*good/bad, acceptable/unacceptable, friend/enemy, superior/inferior, strong/weak, useful/useless, cool/not cool, in/out?* Read the categories and their examples below. Then write categories and examples of your own. Be fearless—and nonjudgmental—in compiling your lists.

CATEGORY: **(Good) Healthy drinks**	**EXAMPLES:** **water, herbal tea, organic milk**
CATEGORY: **(Bad) Unhealthy drinks**	**EXAMPLES:** **coffee, alcohol, sugary sodas**
CATEGORY:	EXAMPLES:
CATEGORY:	EXAMPLES:
CATEGORY:	EXAMPLES:
CATEGORY:	EXAMPLES:

Which of your judgments do you think *most* people would agree with?
Which would few agree with? Suppose you reversed the items in each category. Use the space below to make a case for a contrasting point of view, such as organic milk is *not* a healthy drink.

____

____

____

____

____

____

Judgment loops. We've all fallen into this trap: we're in a new situation; we're feeling anxious and unsure of ourselves. Before we know it, our mind has generated a mini-drama. We feel helplessly drawn into the drama. For instance, a man we'll call Ted has made a date with a woman he connected with on an online dating site. The two are meeting in person for the first time, at a local restaurant. Ted hasn't been to this restaurant before. It took a while for him to find the restaurant, and then to find a parking space. At this point, he's feeling a mixture of excitement, curiosity, and frustration over being late. He's sweating a little.

Ted walks into the restaurant and is met with a wall of noise—loud music and a crowd of chattering people at the bar. He feels disoriented. The restaurant has an air of elegance. Most of the patrons seem to have stepped out of the pages of a fashion magazine. Now he's really feeling uncomfortable. As he stands in the entryway trying to find his date, here's what's going through his mind:

- "This isn't my kind of place."
- "I don't fit in."
- "Everybody's looking at me. They can see what a dork I am. They're laughing at me."
- "My date has probably seen me and is hiding."
- "I should just leave."

Poor Ted. He's completely lost in a negative judgment loop. And poor us when we let anxiety, fear, and insecurity get the better of us and sabotage our good sense.

1.3.4

- As you read about Ted's situation, could you relate to any aspects of it? Which aspects?______

____

____

____

____

- Using your own experience and the information we've covered so far in the book, list some ways that Ted could have calmed himself and avoided falling victim to the self-defeating monologue in his mind. ____________________

____

____

____

- Describe the last time you were caught in a negative thought loop.

____

____

____

____

Procrastination. We've all succumbed to procrastination. When we have an unpleasant task to do—or something else we'd *rather* do—our mind plays the "later" game. It whispers seductively, "Don't worry about working on those taxes right now. It's Saturday. You can work on them tomorrow. Or the day after that, or..." Here are some other examples.

"After the holidays, I'll cut down on my drinking."

"When this work project is finished, I'll begin an exercise program."

"I'll visit my parents next month."

"That messy closet can wait another month or two."

1.3.5

List three things you've recently put off until "later." Describe how you rationalized postponing these tasks or activities.

1. I postponed ______________________________

____

____

Rationalization: ______________________________

____

____

____

2. I postponed ______________________________

____

____

Rationalization: ______________________________

____

____

____

3. I postponed ______________________________

____

____

Rationalization: ______________________________

____

____

____

The river of denial. One of the great mind games is denial. When there's something too painful, too embarrassing, too difficult, or too inconvenient to face, the mind helps us ignore it. That would be well and good—except that ignorance is a dark, damp, unpleasant place.

Have you noticed that life has a way of trying to bring us out of denial and into truth? A person or a situation will eventually place us face to face with what we're denying. But we often close our eyes and return to our cell of denial. It takes a great deal of courage and self-compassion to emerge from the darkness of ignorance into the light of truth.

1.3.6 We have to reach deeply into ourselves to identify and confront what we're denying. This often requires the help of a skilled therapist, analyst, or other guide. For this exercise, write about a time when you were able to become aware of and face a truth you denied. Note the most important aspects of this discovery. Describe ways that you changed as a result of facing this truth.

CHAPTER

4 Changing Our Mind

The comparison of the mind to a library has its limits. In an actual library, we're free to choose specific books and periodicals. Library personnel don't inundate us with things we do not want. However, we often feel as though we have no choice over the items that our mind presents to us. Another important difference is that librarians weed out materials no longer of use to their patrons. But the collections in our mind-library remain forever.

Let's stay with this analogy for some further insights. Actual libraries have "hold shelves." These shelves contain books that library patrons have requested and that are ready for pickup. Libraries also have shelves in central locations that contain often-used books such as reference books or current best sellers.

Yoga teaches that we can create "hold shelves" and ready-reference shelves in our minds. We can place desirable thoughts on these shelves for easy access. Just as an actual library would not place unnecessary, undesirable, or unhelpful books on these shelves, we would not place unnecessary, undesirable, or unhelpful thoughts on our mind's "hold shelves." Such thoughts can be sent to the basement of our mind-library, to a less-accessible location.

In other words, Yoga teaches that

- we have *choices* with regard to our thoughts; we are not helpless victims of them
- we can replace unhelpful thoughts with helpful thoughts
- we can readily access peaceful and pleasant thoughts

This can be done through a practice of *Kriyā Yoga*. *Kriyā* means "action." The Yoga of action is composed of effort, reflection, and surrender of the fruits of our actions.

- **Effort** (*tapas*) is the discipline or willpower to stay on the peaceful path, rather than acting on the mind's whimsy.
- **Reflection** (*svādhyāya*) consists of reframing where you currently are in life, as well as moving closer to a truer you through self-reflection, which leads to self-knowledge.
- **Excellence in action** (*iśvarapranidhāna*) refers to focusing on the *quality* of our actions, rather than on their *results*. This is what is meant by surrendering the fruits of our actions.

Kriyā Yoga helps us reduce our suffering while manifesting peace. Proactive practices are inherent in the "Yoga of Action." They include *āsana, prāṇāyāma*, and meditation, which together change the quality of our thoughts for the better.

Āsana (movement). The purposes of *āsana* are to:

- create compassionate communication between the mind and body through the breath
- release pent-up tensions and anxieties in order to help settle the mind
- create ease and strength in the body, for daily life and seated meditation

In Exercise 1.2.5, you experienced *āsana*—movement within the breath—in which you raised and lowered your arms. The next exercise expands on that *āsana*.

1.4.1

EXERCISE 1.4.1

Stand with your back straight but not rigid. Rest your arms at your sides. Alternatively, sit in a chair that allows you to straighten your back. Use *ujjayi* breathing in this exercise if you can do so comfortably. After the exercise, note your observations.

1. Begin inhaling slowly. After a second or two, slowly begin raising your arms, forward and up, as you continue to inhale. Raise the arms as high as they will comfortably extend and then allow the inhale to finish.
2. Begin exhaling slowly, drawing the abdomen in and upward. After a second or two, slowly bend your body forward and extend your fingertips forward and then down toward your toes. Finish the movement just before the exhale ends.
3. Begin inhaling slowly. After a second or two, begin raising your arms and then your torso all the way up to a standing position, with your arms extended toward the ceiling, as you continue to inhale.
4. Begin exhaling, and slowly lower your arms to your sides.
5. Take two or three easy breaths. Then repeat, for a total of three to six forward bends.

Write about your experience of *āsana*. Describe your state of mind, physical sensations, and any other feelings during the *āsana*.

EXERCISE 1.4.1

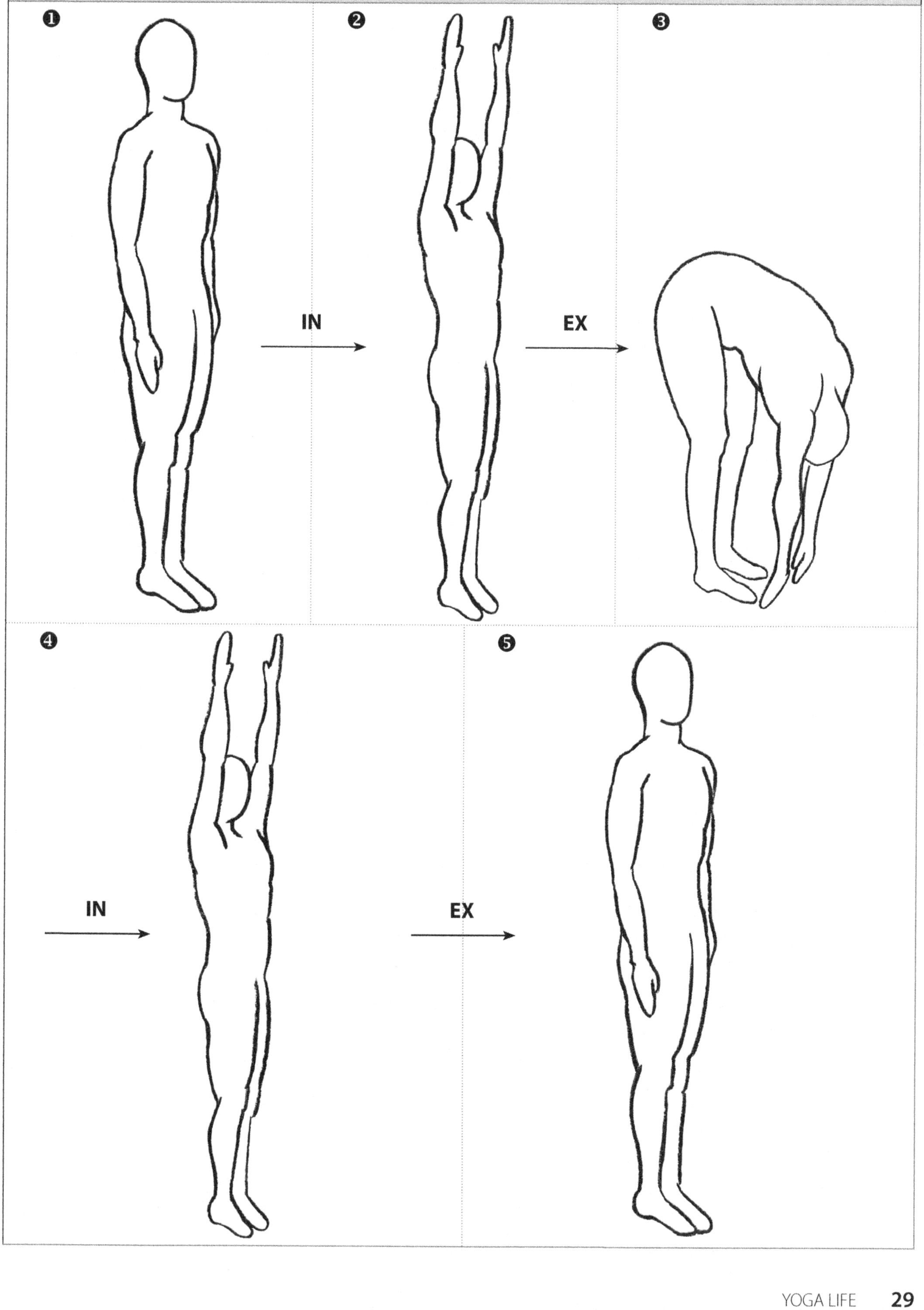

Prāṇāyāma (awareness and regulation of the breath).

The purposes of *prānṇāyāma* are to:

- create a gateway between the mind and body
- encourage quiet direction of thoughts, which creates a sense of the self as an observer who can simply witness our thoughts, rather than identify with each passing thought
- provide a gateway to meditation by encouraging a still body and conscious breathing

We often take a deep breath to soothe distress or anxiety. This shows that we already know that the breath influences our mind and emotions (and vice versa). In Yoga we can use *prāṇāyāma* daily to make better choices about which thoughts to respond to, rather than reacting impulsively.

In Exercises 1.1.7, 1.2.3, and 1.2.4, you experienced conscious breathing and control of the breath. The next exercise offers an experience of *prāṇāyāma* in which we inhale through one nostril, and exhale with *ujjayi*.

EXERCISE 1.4.2

1.4.2

You will use the thumb and the ring finger (the one nearest the "pinkie" finger) of the right hand to alternate closing each nostril. (Curl your "pointer" finger and middle finger inward, toward the hand.) To close the right nostril, place the thumb just to the right of the bridge of the nose. Now *gently* "draw down" so that the right nostril is blocked. To close the left nostril, place the ring finger just to the left of the bridge of the nose and gently draw down. Experiment with this a few times until you feel comfortable with it.

Sit with a straight back. For *viloma prāṇāyāma* we will not do *ujjayi* breathing on the inhale. Instead, we will just breathe in through the nostrils.

❶ Place your right hand near your nose, with the pointer finger and middle finger curled inward. Rest your thumb lightly on the right nostril; rest your ring finger lightly on the left nostril.

❷ Use your thumb to block the right nostril. Inhale slowly through the left nostril.

❸ Release the hand placement, and exhale using *ujjayi*.

❹ Use your ring finger to block the left nostril. Inhale slowly through the right nostril.

❺ Release the hand placement, and exhale using *ujjayi*. Repeat steps 2–5 six to eight more times.

Write about your experience of this *prāṇāyāma* technique. Describe your state of mind, physical sensations, and any other feelings during the *prāṇāyāma*.

EXERCISE 1.4.2

1.4.2

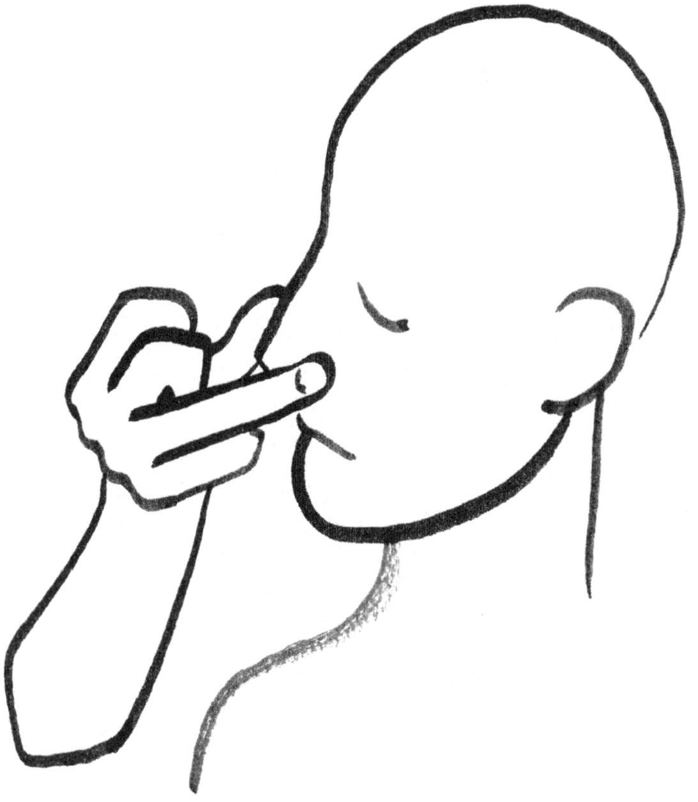

Meditation (cultivating a quiet and peaceful mind). The purpose of Yoga is to direct the thoughts of the mind, and meditation is where we actively practice this. Think of meditation as strength training for your mind. It is an active exercise of directing our mind toward specific objects, words, images, or thoughts. A regular practice of meditation cultivates the strength to better direct our thoughts in everyday life.

1.4.3

In a comfortable seated position, in a quiet room, take a few slow, easy breaths. When you feel settled, set a timer for 4 minutes.

Sit as still as possible, breathing normally. Notice any desire to move, scratch an itch, wet the lips, or swallow. Move when necessary, but do so with full attention.

While you are sitting, allow the mind's stream of thoughts to flow. (Trying to stop the flow is impossible.) When you notice that the mind has become stuck on a thought—a commentary on the experience of sitting still, or an idea, memory, or plan—bring it gently back to the sense of stillness in your body.

When the timer sounds, continue to be quiet. Slowly stretch your legs, either in the seated position or lying on your back.

Then write about your experience. Describe your state of mind, physical sensations, and other feelings during the meditation.

The smile in your mind. The practices of *āsana, prāṇāyāma*, and meditation can produce a sense of peace, or even joy. One of my teachers, Ganesh Mohan likens the feeling to a "smile in your mind." Isn't that a nice concept? Just thinking about a smile in your mind can bring about a smile on your face.

1.4.4

In a comfortable seated position, in a quiet room, take a few slow, easy breaths. Then, with your eyes gently closed, imagine a smile in your mind. Try to hold the smile in your mind for a few moments. Notice whether you also have a slight smile on your face.

After a few minutes, gently open your eyes and write about your experience.

- Were you able to sense the smile in your mind? ____________________

____

____

____

____

- If so, was there a particular feeling or image associated with it ? ____________________

____

____

____

____

- How long did the smile last? Did it come and go? ____________________

____

____

____

____

- What else did you notice during this exercise? ____________________

____

____

____

____

If you were able to access the "smile in your mind" during the exercise, you can try it under different conditions—such as during work, on a bus or subway, while walking on a city street, or in a noisy restaurant. You can also try to access the smile during moments when you feel anxious, angry, or fearful.

Tens of thousands of thoughts. Strength training for the mind begins with simply noticing our thoughts. It's not possible, or even desirable, to be completely attentive to our thoughts in every waking moment. But for the next few days, notice the nature of your thoughts during activities such as the ones below. Notice both the content and the categories of the thoughts, such as judging, planning, remembering, imagining, and organizing. Try to keep a certain distance from the thoughts, but be completely accepting of them. Observe your thoughts as a scientist would.

1.4.5

For each activity that applies to you, summarize what you noticed about your thoughts during the activity.

- Waking from sleep: ______
- Exercising: ______
- Eating a meal: ______
- Doing an *āsana* practice: ______
- Talking to a loved one: ______
- Getting ready for bed: ______
- Other activity: ______

Were you amazed at your range of thoughts? Of course, deliberately *noticing* your thoughts affects the *quality* of the thoughts. The Commentator in our mind says, "Oh, look—she's watching her thoughts!" The Monitor says, "Oops, forgot what we were doing. Must return to watching the thoughts." Not wanting to be left out, the Analyst says, "Hmmm, you're very hard on yourself. Wonder why?" And so on.

Be kind to yourself when doing strength training for the mind—even when your thoughts gallop through your mind like a team of wild horses.

Now, let's experiment with focusing our thoughts.

1.4.6

Choose a daily activity such as brushing your teeth, washing dishes, or eating a meal as a focus for this exercise. Before doing the activity, set an intention to bring conscious attention to it. When your mind wanders, gently lead it back to the activity.

- What activity did you choose?____________________
- What did you notice when you *first* began the activity?____________________
- What did you notice *during* the activity?____________________
- What did you notice *after* the activity? ____________________

Using a *mantra*. Another step in strength training for the mind is to employ a *mantra* to help engage our attention. *Mantra* literally means "mind protect." A *mantra* can be a sound, syllable, word, or group of words. In Yoga, we use a *mantra* to bring about a peaceful feeling, which then protects us from unhelpful or disturbing thoughts.

The Sanskrit word *Śanti* (SHAHN•tee), meaning "peace," is a common *mantra* in a Yoga practice. We can use *Śanti* to protect our minds from unhelpful thoughts in the following exercise.

1.4.7

Find a quiet space without distractions. Take a comfortable seated position. Relax by taking a few easy breaths. If possible, set a timer for 5, 6, or 7 minutes. Then follow this breathing pattern:

- On the inhale, mentally say the first syllable of *Śanti*: "Śan"
- On the exhale, mentally say the second syllable of *Śanti*: "ti"
- Continue in this way until the time is up. Rather than translate *Śanti* to yourself as "peace," just enjoy the sound of the syllables as you breathe.
- What did you notice, mentally and physically, *during* this exercise? ____________________
- Did you experience any resistance to the exercise? If so, explain ____________________
- What did you notice *after* the exercise?____________________

Using an image. A pleasant image can help bring our mind to a peaceful state. Particularly helpful are images of things found in nature—trees, waterfalls, sunsets, flowers. In fact, several studies have shown that hospital patients need less pain medication and recover more quickly when they have access to scenes of nature through a window or courtyard, or through art on the walls.

Let's continue to explore bringing focus to our mind. This time we'll use an object or an image.

1.4.8

Find a quiet space, free of interruptions. Choose an object or image that has a pleasant and serene quality—preferably something from nature, such as a leaf, rock, or flower, or a photograph or artwork that shows a peaceful natural scene. Set a timer for one minute.

- Place the object or image on a table or other surface in front of you.
- Sit in a comfortable position.
- Let your eyes rest on the object or image as you allow your breath to come and go naturally.
- Allow your thoughts to come and go, without attaching to them. Just keep your focus on the object or image. Do not try too hard to do anything. Simply allow yourself to be absorbed by the object or image.
- You may want to repeat the name of the object or image in your mind as you gaze.

Continue in this way until the time is up. Then write about your experience.

- What did you notice, mentally and physically, during this exercise?________________

- Did you experience any resistance to the exercise? If so, explain ________________

- Did your attitude toward the object or image change during the exercise? If so, explain _____

PART 2

THE FIVE ACTIVITIES OF THE MIND (*VṚTTI*)

In Part 1 we explored the central message of Yoga:

yoga citta vṛtti nirodha

citta—our conscious mind

vṛtti—our thoughts, or the activities of the mind

nirodha—to direct

Yoga is the ability to direct our thoughts.

According to Patanjali's *Yoga Sūtras*, there are five activities, or "movements," of the mind. These are our *vṛtti*. A practice of Yoga cultivates awareness of these activities, which then guides our conscious *vṛtti* toward balance and weakens compulsive thinking and behavior.

The five types of mental activities include thoughts, experiences, and emotions. These activities can lead us down a path toward problems or onto one of peace.

- ***pramāna***—correct understanding that does not change
- ***viparyaya***—incorrect understanding that may change with time
- ***vikalpa***—imagination
- ***nidrā***—deep sleep/knowledge of sleep
- ***smṛti***—memory

CHAPTER

5

Correct Understanding (*Pramāna*)

Our nature is to desire accurate, unchanging knowledge. When we observe the mind, we notice thoughts changing from moment to moment so quickly that we can scarcely question their validity. And even if we could examine each passing thought, how can we ensure that our understanding or knowledge is accurate? Often our senses guide us toward correct understanding—especially when our minds are calm and clear.

According to Yoga, we acquire correct understanding in three different ways.

1. **Direct perception:** by directly experiencing—through our senses of sight, hearing, taste, smell, and touch—an object or a phenomenon when the mind is focused. For instance, a marble surface feels cold to the touch, and the smell of spoiled milk has a pungent odor. We can be assured that these facts are true because we have experienced the truth of them.
2. **Inference:** by using previous knowledge (from direct perception), as well as logic, to draw a conclusion. For example, after it has snowed, we might infer that the roads will be slick, even though we haven't been on them yet. We're basing our inference on our previous experience of driving after a snowfall.
3. **Testimony:** by hearing or reading the words of an authoritative source. For instance, we can be fairly certain of the accuracy of a declaration made by a witness under oath, or a Sherpa's account of climbing the Himalayas.

The daily practice of Yoga leads us toward correct understanding. We begin to see ourselves and others more clearly and honestly. We begin to view events and situations as they are, rather than as we wish them to be. We become more curious and welcoming toward our inner and outer experiences. We become more able to tolerate change and uncertainty.
When practiced according to the wisdom of the *Yoga Sūtras*, Yoga removes the obstacles to our correct understanding, our *pramāna*.

2.5.1 What is an example of *correct understanding* or *correct knowledge* you have gained through direct perception, inference, or testimony? ______________________________

____

____

____

How did you acquire this understanding or knowledge—by direct perception, inference, or testimony? ______________________________

____

____

____

Correct knowledge is not in and of itself "good" or "bad." Such knowledge can affect us emotionally—we can feel happiness or comfort, as well as pain and discomfort, as a result of coming to correct understanding. But that doesn't make it inherently "good" or "bad." When we practice Yoga for a time, we learn to meet *pramāna* from a position of calmness and steadiness—as well as gratitude—because it places us on solid ground.

Remaining neutral helps us discern correct knowledge. When we observe events without attaching judgments or story lines to them, we're better able to perceive what is true and what is not true.

The following ancient story illustrates the value of staying neutral in the face of external events. By remaining open and curious, we are better able to recognize *pramāna*.

2.5.2

A farmer had a horse that had served him well for several years. One day, however, the horse ran away. When the farmer's neighbors heard about this, they came to see the farmer. "How terrible!" they cried. "Such bad luck!"

"We shall see," replied the farmer.

The next day, the farmer's horse returned, accompanied by three wild horses. "Now you have four horses!" said the farmer's neighbors. "Such good luck!"

"We shall see," replied the farmer.

The day after that, when the farmer's son was trying to ride one of the wild horses, the horse threw him. The young man broke his leg in the fall. "A broken leg," said the neighbors, shaking their heads. "What bad luck!"

"We shall see," replied the farmer.

The very next day, military officers came to the village to recruit young men to serve in the army. Because the farmer's son had a broken leg, the officers did not take the boy. "Congratulations," cried the neighbors. "Your son has been spared. How wonderful!"

"We shall see," replied the farmer.

In your opinion, what is the lesson in this story? How does it relate to *pramāna*?

CHAPTER

6

Incorrect Understanding (*Viparyaya*)

We are in a state of *viparyaya*—incorrect understanding—when our senses or our thoughts are mistaken or misguided. In Chapter 3, we explored some of the ways that our minds can deceive us—for example, in mistaking a rope for a snake.

Sometimes we make something solid out of our prejudices, opinions, and emotions. We label them as "true" or "correct" in order to feel safe and secure. Then we find ourselves defending these hardened truths against the conflicting truths of others. No wonder there's so much drama in our lives!

We all see forwarded emails that present supposedly true stories. *"CDC says don't get flu shots this year!" . . . "New study shows coffee aids weight loss!" . . . "Eating chocolate reduces the risk of heart disease!"* None of these are *pramāna*. Even when so-called facts are based on a study, we must look carefully at details of the study, such as its length, design, and number and types of participants. We should be careful about accepting and passing along incorrect and untrue information. And we should be just as skeptical of our own "true stories." To paraphrase an old saying: *It's not the things we don't know that get us into trouble; it's those things that we "know for sure" (but are actually not so) that get us into trouble.*

One way to bring ourselves out of the state of *viparyaya* and into *pramāna* is to question what we think we know: How do I know it's true? What's the source? Can I be absolutely certain this knowledge is true?

Another way to move from *viparyaya* to *pramāna* is to notice our reaction when someone else challenges our true story. Do we become angry or defensive? Do we feel attacked? Strong, emotional reactions such as these are important clues. They suggest that our knowledge or understanding may be incorrect.

2.6.1

Viparyaya comes to us in many forms. We know that when our mind is clear, our senses can lead us to *pramāna* (correct knowledge). But our senses sometimes deceive us and lead us to *viparyaya*, particularly in judgments about others—*she's self-centered . . . he doesn't care about my feelings . . . they can't be trusted.* Think about someone with whom you've experienced difficulty. What opinion or conclusion have you formed about that person, based on your interactions with him or her? In the space below, state your opinion or conclusion. Then list at least two reasons for your point of view. Next, review what you have written. Circle any words or phrases that someone else might consider *viparyaya*.

Challenging what we think we know is difficult and courageous work. Sometimes we'd rather examine the *viparyaya* of others, rather than our own. But *viparyaya* offers us an opportunity to wake up. It's also an occasion to practice compassion toward ourselves and others.

2.6.2

This exercise offers a chance to generate a sense of compassion toward yourself.

First, place your hands at your heart, take a deep breath in and let it out, feeling the life inside.

Next, inhale, opening your arms wide. As you exhale, hug yourself. Then inhale, fold your hands over your heart again, and exhale.

Do this several times. Focus attention on how you would comfort yourself if you were sad or grieving. If you're not used to soothing yourself in this way, the exercise may seem odd at first. Try it anyhow, and write about how this form of self-compassion could create a new level of tenderness toward yourself.

CHAPTER

7

Imagination (*Vikalpa*)

Vikalpa refers to knowledge that is not based on a corresponding object. The term is summarized in the words "imagination" or "fantasy." According to the *Yoga Sūtras*, *vikalpa* refers less to artistic creative imagination and more to made-up scenarios of our future, or ways to avoid discomfort in the present.

Instead of being present during a stressful meeting, we imagine ourselves elsewhere—getting a cocktail, eating ice cream, going on vacation . . . anything to avoid engaging with what's happening at that moment.

We also use our imagination to indulge in worst-case scenarios . . . *It's midnight, and my teenage daughter was supposed to be home an hour ago. Something terrible must have happened . . . The prospective employer said I'd hear by Tuesday if I got the job, but it's Thursday and I've heard nothing from him.*

Obviously, I didn't get the job. I may never get a job . . .

2.7.1 For part of the day, observe how you use your imagination to create "alternative realities" or spin fantasies. Do not judge yourself or struggle against your imagination. Simply witness it. Make notes about the circumstances and content of your imaginings, as though you were a social scientist. Note whether you imagined pleasant scenarios or unpleasant ones.

Remember that, as with the other *vṛttis*, *vikalpa* is not something you must try to extinguish. The *vṛttis* are descriptive: they simply categorize the activities our mind is capable of. They help us awaken to our mind. Yoga helps us recognize the *vṛtti* we are in when, for example, we experience pain. It offers us a way to reframe our experience and discover what is true and what ultimately leads us to peace. In the exercise below, we explore maintaining *vikalpa*.

2.7.2 Observe your mind during parts of the day. When you notice that your imagination has taken you out of the present moment, *gently* say—aloud or silently—"here, now. "Take three or four slow, easy breaths. Then go on about your business. What did you observe about this sequence?

CHAPTER

8 Knowledge of Sleep (*Nidrā*)

You may be familiar with the term *nidrā* as a restful visualization practice, or guided relaxation. This is a modern, Westernized concept of *nidrā*. According to the *Yoga Sūtras*, *nidrā* is a unique state in which the four other types of *vṛtti* are absent. It is often referred to as "knowledge of sleep."

In Part 1, Chapter 1, we discovered that the mind's job is to think, which means it is continuously darting among different *vṛtti*. The goal of Yoga is to direct the *vṛtti*. In deep and dreamless sleep the mind is not moving from thought to thought. The mind is also not consciously directing *vṛtti*, either. That is why sleep is considered its own special *vṛtti*—a deep level of awareness in which the attention is absorbed in the negation of the other four *vṛtti*. Metaphorically, it is as if the mind is focused on an immense darkness. Upon waking, we have a memory of having slept well or unwell, and an immediate identification with our thoughts . . . from the prior day, week, or all the way back to our first cognitions.

The following analogy may help. Imagine that you are watching images in a film. Suddenly the screen goes dark for a few moments. Then the light and images return and you recall what you had seen before the screen went dark. The darkness represents your mind when you're asleep.

2.8.1

Tomorrow morning, as you awaken, focus awareness on the quality of your sleep. Do you have the sense of having slept well, or not well? Why do you think this is so? Next, become aware of states of *vṛtti* that arise in your mind. Are you planning your day? Recalling a dream? Orienting yourself in time by checking the clock? Making predictions?

In the space below, write about your quality of sleep. Then briefly describe the states of *vṛtti* that you experienced in the first moments after waking up.

____

____

____

____

____

____

____

____

CHAPTER

9

Memory (*Smṛti*)

Smṛti, like *vikalpa* (imagination), is a common mind state. It refers to our stored experiences and observations. In any moment, we are either retrieving a memory or being surprised by a memory. Our responses to present experiences are often governed by our memories, which can be pleasant, unpleasant, or neutral. We store some of our memories so deeply that we're not conscious of them.

Here are a few examples of how memories can influence our current behavior:

My mother wore lilac perfume, so every time I smell lilacs I think of her.

A teacher once told me I was "scatterbrained," so I use that as an excuse when I can't focus.

I once got sick after eating lobster, so I can never again eat lobster.

2.9.1

Think of a pleasant memory that you often return to. Describe the memory below. ____________

____

____

What is special about this memory? ____________

____

____

____

Does recalling this memory produce physical sensations in you? If so, describe these sensations below. ____________

____

____

____

What is an example of an unpleasant memory that you voluntarily or involuntarily recall? ____________

____

____

____

What are the circumstances in which this recollection happens ____________

____

____

What, if any, physical sensations does the memory produce in you? ____________

____

____

Have you ever recalled a shared memory with a partner, a close friend, or a sibling and noticed that some details of the shared memory differ between you? *Not true—I was wearing the red dress, not the blue one . . . It happened on Tuesday morning, not Wednesday night . . . You must be mistaken—We've never eaten at that cafe . . .*

These differing recollections show us that our memories aren't always accurate. In other words, they can be a form of *viparyaya*, or incorrect knowledge. Studies of eyewitnesses to traffic accidents and other events confirm that our memories are highly individual and therefore highly selective. That's all right—it's just how we're constructed.

A few lines from the song "I Remember It Well," from the musical *Gigi*, delightfully illustrate our selective memories.

He: We met at nine.

She: *We met at eight.*

He: I was on time.

She: *No, you were late.*

He: Ah, yes, I remember it well. We dined with friends.

She: *We dined alone.*

He: A tenor sang.

She: *A baritone.*

He: Ah, yes, I remember it well. That dazzling April moon!

She: *There was none that night, and the month was June.*

He: That's right. That's right.

She: *It warms my heart to know that you remember still the way you do.*

He: Ah, yes, I remember it well.

PART 3

CAUSES OF SUFFERING (*Kleśas*)

Suffering is an inevitable part of being human. In the Yogic sense, "suffering" refers more to mental rather than physical afflictions. Just as the ancient Yoga sages identified five *vṛtti,* or states of mind, they identified five *kleśas*, or common causes of human affliction. The *kleśas* are:

- ***avidyā***—illusion
- ***asmitā***—"I am-ness," over-identification with the intellect and the body
- ***rāga***—attachment to pleasure
- ***dveṣa***—aversion to pain
- ***abhiniveśa***—fear

Kleśas can cause suffering, but they are also part of who we are as humans. We seek pleasurable experiences and try to avoid painful ones. Sometimes a *kleśa* such as *abhiniveśa* (fear) aids us in self-protection, but at other times, it can cause deep suffering. In the face of so many distractions nowadays, we can unconsciously cycle from one *kleśa* to the next. The *kleśas* are not behaviors or cognitions that we can necessarily control.

This section of the book is intended to help us cultivate awareness of the *kleśas*, label them, and see how our thoughts and behaviors are driven by them. Then in Part 4 we will look into our behaviors through the *Yamas* and *Niyamas*. Our goal will be to see the link between our actions and our thoughts, a link that can lessen the unconscious driving force of the *kleśas*.

What does this have to do with our Yoga practice? The purpose of our Yoga practice is to gain insight into our thinking and our behavior. Such insight has the power to weaken the effect of the *kleśas*, so that we can have more peace in our daily lives.

CHAPTER

10 Illusion (*Avidyā*)

I saw the moon moving in the sky. Then I understood that it was merely the wind blowing clouds across its outline.

Avidyā is the source of the other *kleśas*. It is called the "root of all suffering." *Avidyā* is the illusion that we know the real nature of things. But we are often confused about what is true or false, pure or impure, temporary or permanent.

Avidyā creates the illusion that we're separate from everything and everyone else. It also creates the illusion that we have complete control of our lives.

Having clouded perception does not mean that we're deficient or flawed. When we examine our versions of *avidyā*, we find that our motives are not bad. We're simply holding on to illusions in order to avoid pain—or, in some cases, to survive.

One example of *avidyā* is a culture-driven illusion that we get happiness acquiring externals (a new car, the latest electronic gadget, anti-wrinkle cream, and so on). We also have a familiar saying: "It's what's on the inside that counts. "These messages contradict each other. How can both be true?

Looking outside ourselves for fulfillment can create temporary satisfaction, but we must look inside ourselves to create lasting fulfillment. It's exciting to have a new car, but the excitement fades when the car breaks down or someone rear-ends it. One kind of happiness depends on the state of our material goods. The other, everlasting kind is independent of external events and conditions.

All of the world's wisdom traditions—including Yoga—teach that when we shift from the pursuit of external goods to the pursuit of inner goods, such as steadiness, peace, and generosity, we begin to live at deeper levels of acceptance and contentment.

3.10.1

In this exercise, we'll explore how we fall prey to the feeling that something outside us will solve a problem or give us more happiness. We can use a simple equation:

If I had more stylish sunglasses, I'd be more confident.

If I had a child, I'd be more fulfilled

List some of your own equations:

1. ______________________________

____

2. ______________________________

____

3. ______________________________

____

Let's burrow a little deeper as we explore our tendency to look for externals to give us a sense of satisfaction.

3.10.2

For the next few weeks, notice when your mind is reaching for externals such as food, clothing, or other items to fill an emotional need or solve a problem.
We're not trying to change anything, at this point. We're just noting how our mind works in this regard. Take note of three examples from your life in the space below.

1. What did you notice your mind reaching for? ______

   What was the time of day this occurred? ______

   What was the situation, and what were you feeling? ______

2. What did you notice your mind reaching for? ______

   What was the time of day this occurred? ______

   What was the situation, and what were you feeling? ______

3. What did you notice your mind reaching for? ______

   What was the time of day this occurred? ______

   What was the situation, and what were you feeling? ______

Another example of *avidyā* is the tendency to cling to our opinions and beliefs about the world. Sometimes we state our opinions as facts, when in truth they are simply views, judgments, or appraisals. At times our attachment to our beliefs can blind us from seeing other perspectives. This can cause conflict in our relationships and in society.

It is always good to gently question our thinking. "Where did my understanding come from?" or "Is this *really* true?" You might ask, "Am I holding on to this belief too closely and ignoring other ideas that could expand my understanding?" The path of Yoga guides us to remain open to all points of view. This helps us reduce the suffering from the illusion that our point of view is the only valid one.

Television, social media, and the Internet provide a steady stream of opinions dressed up as facts. Fortunately, it's not that difficult to fact-check product claims, rumors, or political statements. There are many reputable Websites devoted to confirming or debunking public information.

In the next two exercises we will look at the beliefs of others as well as our own.

3.10.3

For a few days, pay close attention to statements presented as true facts. Write three examples in the space below. Include statements that you know are not true, those of which you're unsure, and those that you know to be true.

1. Untrue statement presented as truth:______________________________

2. Statement not yet proven true or false: ______________________________

3. Statement that can be proven to be true: ______________________________

3.10.4

For a day or two, monitor the truths or supposed truths you tell others. List a few of these below. Also note whether you feel frustration or sadness when others don't agree with your version of the truth.

1. What I tell others as the truth: ______________________________

   How I feel when others challenge this truth:____________________

2. What I tell others as the truth ______________________________

   How I feel when others challenge this truth:____________________

3. What I tell others as the truth ______________________________

   How I feel when others challenge this truth: ____________________

Because it is so easy for us to mistake illusion for reality, we must be alert to our thinking and to what we tell others. Here are some questions you can ask yourself to test your own ways of thinking, to avoid illusion:

- Is what I think true in every possible instance?
- What is the source of this belief?
- When did I first acquire this belief?
- What influenced it?

Could someone else have a different point of view regarding this belief? Could their point of view be just as valid as mine?

CHAPTER

11

Overidentification with the Intellect and the Body (*Asmitā*)

Asmitā is the illusion that our intellect and our bodies are our sole forms of consciousness. This is akin to mistaking the filament in a light bulb as the source of its light.

This *kleśa*, a cause of affliction, is frequently defined as "*I am*-ness"—such as, "*I am* a Yoga teacher" or "*I am* a college graduate." At its most basic, *asmitā* is "I AM"—a basic awareness of our existence as discrete individuals. The *content* of the "I am's" varies from person to person, but the *structure* is the same in everyone. Except when we're in deep sleep, we are all conscious of our "I am-ness." This sense pervades all our actions, but it is not wholly negative. It helps us create and accomplish goals.

Asmitā is often confused with ego. Did you know that ego is the Latin word for "I"? You may have heard it said that if someone always uses "I" at the beginning of his sentences, he may have an inflated ego. A client of mine frequently says, "one could" instead of "I could," but that can lead to disassociating from emotions and feelings.

For the purposes of this workbook, by "ego" I mean our sense of self-importance or self-worth as contrasted with the importance or worth of others and the world. While *asmitā* is not solely the opinion we have about ourselves, it does lead to our sense of ourselves. *Asmitā* helps us survive and avoid pain; it orients us in space and time; and it helps us differentiate, recognize, and respond in order to get along in society.

3.11.1

Begin an insightful practice of your sense of "I am-ness" by being mindful of (that is, noticing without harsh judgment) how frequently you use "I" in your conversations today. Be attentive when you share your beliefs, opinions, and stories. Gently assess three "I" statements you make, as in these examples:

My statement contributed in a positive way to the conversation.

My statement caused an uncomfortable silence.

My statement offered a way to connect with others' experiences.

1. "I" statement: ______________________________

   My assessment of the statement and its effect: ______________________________

   ____

2. "I" statement: ______________________________

   My assessment of the statement and its effect: ______________________________

   ____

3. "I" statement: ______________________________

   My assessment of the statement and its effect: ______________________________

   ____

Our "deeper self" has also been described as a "soul," "spirit," and "silent observer." We cannot see it, hear it, or touch it. Nevertheless, it is something we sense within us. Using the space below, describe one or more experiences in which you had a sense of your deeper self.

3.11.2

Asmitā also creates over-identification with our physical bodies. It is good for us to value our body, as the following poem expresses:

Time was when I despised the body;

But then I saw the God within.

The body, I realized, is the Lord's temple;

And so I began preserving it with care Infinite.

~Bhogar

It's important, though, to remember that we are more substantive than our physical body. We can be grateful for our bodies and nurture them without becoming preoccupied with them or seeking to perfect them.

Asmitā can lead to self-righteousness. We can all fall prey to thinking we know best, or that our way of doing something is *the* way to do it. We tend to solidify what is fluid. Instead of listening and accepting another person's differing point of view, we often plot ways to bring that person to our way of thinking. This usually means we aren't really listening to the other person but are in our heads rehearsing what we're going to say next.

Asmitā can also lead to unhealthy levels of envy and competitiveness. Comparing ourselves with others is not all bad. Seeing a friend or colleague accomplish something admirable can inspire us to greater achievement. But it could also lead to thoughts such as "I have to be better than my co-worker," or "I have to look younger than my contemporaries," and "I have to prove that I am right," or even "I'll show I'm smarter than everyone else in the room."

Asmitā can sometimes be so powerful that we feel as if others are living inside our world, rather than all of us existing in a greater world. The following exercise offers one way to practice being part of a greater world rather than living inside the world of our mind.

3.11.3 Cultivate the ability to see yourself as a small but necessary part of a greater world.

- Awaken at dawn and go outside to watch the sun rise. As you look around at elements of the natural world, try to see yourself as an "equal partner" in that world—not superior or inferior to any element of it. Use the space below to write about your observations.

- When was the last time you felt a deep connection to other people or other aspects of the world, regardless of your similarities to or differences from them? What was the setting of that experience? What physical sensations accompanied the experience?

CHAPTER

12 Attachment to Pleasure (*Rāga*)

Rāga is what is left in our mind after having had a pleasurable experience. Such an experience naturally leaves a desire to have that pleasure again, which leads to an attachment to the pleasure. Many of our wants and desires are not necessary for our survival, but our senses disagree. For example, if we've just had a satisfying meal, and someone offers us cake for dessert, our senses react. We remember the pleasure of having eaten cake before. Our eyes see the cake, our nose smells it, and our mouth salivates. At that point *rāga* can lead us to have the cake, even though we were completely satisfied a moment ago.

Reducing *rāga* involves facing certain temptations and cravings with the knowledge that they won't bring ultimate satisfaction or lasting peace. Sometimes this knowledge "saves" us and sometimes not—we're only human, after all. Our Yoga practice teaches us the wisdom of reining in our senses, for they aren't wise enough to know what leads us to peace.

There's nothing inherently wrong with wanting to repeat a pleasurable experience. We are pleasure-seeking, pain-avoiding beings. But this becomes a problem when pleasure seeking becomes an overriding goal in life, to the exclusion of everything else.

3.12.1

Notice how the sense of sight drives your desire. For example: *On a walk down a city street, you're not thinking about clothes, but you pass a store window and see a beautiful rain jacket in the window display. Suddenly, you have a strong desire to own the jacket.*

Why would purchasing the jacket feel good? Is it because you have bought clothing before and it lifted your spirits? Is it because you don't have a rain jacket?

For the next few days, notice moments in which your desire for something is fueled by what you see. In the space below, describe these moments and note whether the desire comes from a longing that you've experienced in the past.

Reducing *rāga* is a lifelong pursuit. We may successfully resist a craving in one moment, only to find another one arising in the next moment. Reducing *rāga* means strengthening practices and habits that lead us to peace, rather than to momentary pleasure. Since we are pleasure-seeking beings, we can use *rāga* to our advantage in meditation practice. Let's talk about how to do this.

If we undertake a practice that feels pleasurable, our desire to do the practice again arises in our mind, and we find ourselves becoming attached to our practice. Here one could argue, "But isn't attachment bad? Isn't the goal of our Yoga practice to let go of all attachments?" Yoga encourages us to let go of *superfluous* desires that muddy our minds. Its aim is to promote attachment to practices that lead to tranquility.

3.12.2

What object, person, or thought brings a warm feeling of pleasure in your chest? My clients have mentioned memories of a grandparent, the view from atop a mountain, a feeling of no worries, the smell of lilacs . . . all which gave them feelings of warmth, love, pleasure, and compassion.

Find a quiet place to sit. Choose an object, person, or thought that produces feelings of warmth, love, and/or pleasure. Set a five-minute timer and stay with the feelings for five minutes.

Yoga helps us control strong attachments, desires, and passions that can become compulsions and can consume us. It cultivates a desire for a more genuine and more lasting feeling of satisfaction.

CHAPTER

13 Aversion to Pain (*Dveṣa*)

Dveṣa—aversion or hatred—is the opposite of rāga. When we have an unpleasant experience, dveşa is the impression left in the mind after that experience. We naturally want to avoid repeating such an experience. If we cannot avoid repeating it, we suffer. As with all the *kleśas*, there is a life-preserving aspect to *dveṣa*. We must practice harm avoidance for self-protection and evolution, but untamed *dveşa* causes aversion to pain and its causes. It can produce anger, hatred, and even violence within us.

We see *dveṣa* in full force in the minds of people who commit terrorist acts. A person whose mind is fueled by *dveṣa* can become so enraged that he may not see another way out of his pain other than to harm others. The suffering caused by such acts happens not just to those "in the line of fire" but to whole communities, countries, and even humankind.

Those of us who don't resort to violence can still have our best judgment clouded by *dveṣa*. Unexamined *dveṣa* can keep us in an unhealthy relationship to avoid the pain of a breakup. It can keep us in an unsatisfying job to avoid the discomfort of looking for a new job. The irony is that we keep ourselves miserable through trying to avoid misery.

Dveṣa can also include harboring resentment and revenge fantasies, and being mired in self-pity. Those delusions are a momentary pleasurable aspect of *dveṣa*.

3.13.1

What people, situations, or things do you resist or resent because they are irritating, infuriating, or painful?

Retreat to a quiet place for a half hour or more to consider how *dveṣa* is operating in your life. Then answer the questions below.

- What are you avoiding/resisting/resenting/hating? Why? ______________________

  ____

- How much of your time and/or "mental space" is consumed by this issue? ______________________

  ____

- What physical sensations do you associate with the issue? ______________________

  ____

- What stories do you tell yourself about the issue? What fantasies has your mind generated over it? ______________________

  ____

- How would you complete this statement, concerning the issue:
  If only ____, then I would feel better about this issue ______________________

  ____

  ____

Through *dveṣa* we make ourselves miserable by replaying the memory of an unpleasant experience. Each replay gives the memory more power, and this can lead to conscious or unconscious behaviors in which we try at all costs to avoid repeating the experience. For example, Sam remembers being frightened and angry as a child when his parents argued, and now, as an adult, he has an intense aversion to conflict. He wants the security of a life partner, but he eventually breaks up with each potential partner when there is any conflict. Sam has no insight into his unreasonable aversion toward conflict and no understanding that relationships always involve conflict. Unless he gains insight into this *dveṣa*, he will suffer again and again, because as much as he tries, he cannot avoid the pain of conflict.

3.13.2

Exploring this *kleśa* shows how we learn to make ourselves miserable by holding on to a memory of an unpleasant experience and letting that memory drive our current actions.

Reflect on a *dveṣa* that may exist in your mind now or in the past. Think about how it makes/made you unhappy, and maybe leads/led to loneliness and isolation. Sit quietly and reflect for five to ten minutes. Is there a memory that influenced your feelings about this issue? Write about the memory and its influence.

You have probably heard the saying "Holding hatred toward another person is like swallowing poison and expecting the other person to die." This quote highlights the absurdity of staying mired in *dveṣa*. Our misguided attempts to relieve our pain only cause more pain. This deters us from the path of joy and peace. The tools of Yoga help us recognize and reduce *dveşa* so that we maintain self-protection without turning every unpleasant experience into something to avoid at all costs.

CHAPTER

14 Fear (*Abhiniveśa*)

Abhiniveśa refers to anxiety and fear. We may be fearful of spiders and snakes. We may be anxious about flying. We may be terrified of speaking in public. A basic, shared fear is the fear of dying. Much of our fear keeps us from harm. Other fears can paralyze and defeat us.

We often try to manage fear by removing ourselves from or avoiding a situation, person, or object. This can be healthy, but it can also work against us.

One example of a *healthy* fear is the fear of having an accident while driving. This fear helps us stay alert while driving in order to avoid an accident. An example of an *unhealthy* fear is to be so afraid of the outside world that we rarely leave our home.

Let's take some time to explore our own fears.

3.14.1

List five things that you fear. Briefly explain the reason(s) for each fear. Label the fear "reasonable" or "unreasonable." Then rank its intensity, using a scale of 1 to 10, with 1 being the mildest and 10 the most intense.

1. I fear ______________________________

   because ______________________________

   This fear is (reasonable/unreasonable)______________________________

   Intensity of the fear:______________________________

2. I fear ______________________________

   because ______________________________

   This fear is (reasonable/unreasonable)______________________________

   Intensity of the fear:______________________________

3. I fear ______________________________

   because______________________________

   This fear is (reasonable/unreasonable)______________________________

   Intensity of the fear:______________________________

4. I fear ______________________________

   because______________________________

   This fear is (reasonable/unreasonable)______________________________

   Intensity of the fear:______________________________

5. I fear ______________________________

   because______________________________

   This fear is (reasonable/unreasonable)______________________________

   Intensity of the fear:______________________________

   ____

A common fear is social anxiety. Some social situations provoke anxiety in us, especially unfamiliar situations or ones in which we believe that we're not liked or accepted. This is one reason why many social engagements include alcohol, which lessens inhibitions and relieves us of apprehension.

3.14.2 List three social situations in which you have felt anxious. For each situation, describe the aspect of the situation that caused you the most anxiety. Then describe stories you told yourself before, during, and after the situation.

Situation 1: ______________________

____

____

____

____

Situation 2: ______________________

____

____

____

____

Situation 3: ______________________

____

____

____

____

I was recently hijacked by an unreasonable fear that I had hurt someone. While giving a lecture to new Yoga teachers, I was feeling the usual nervousness that comes with speaking in front of a group. Halfway through my lecture, I noticed that one of the students had become visibly upset. Soon after this, the student fled the room.

I began to scare myself: I feared that I had somehow caused the student's distress and that the other students saw me as a rude and inconsiderate teacher. At the end of my lecture, several participants shared how much they had enjoyed my presentation. Confused, I asked about the missing student. I learned that she had left the room because she was upset over the recent death of her father. What needless suffering I had put myself through! My mild anxiety over speaking in public had been intensified by the student's actions (which had nothing to do with me), which then caused me to jump to conclusions that made me feel even worse.

The calming effects of a Yoga practice help "lower the volume" of our anxieties, fears, and insecurities. Over time, we find ourselves less reactive and less willing to be hooked by our fears. We see situations more clearly and realistically. We're in less of a hurry to put the worst possible spin on a situation or to tell a story that supports our worst fears about ourselves.

Yoga teaches that even though we may never completely escape the influence of the five types of *kleśas*, we can lessen their effects on us. This is very freeing. In recognizing the *kleśas* and understanding our thinking and behavior in terms of them, we can reduce our suffering and increase our peace of mind.

PART 4

ATTITUDES THAT INFLUENCE PEACE IN OUR MINDS (*Yamas and Niyamas*)

In Parts 1 through 3, we explored the territory of our mind. We examined common thought patterns generated by the mind and noticed ways these patterns influence our perspective. In Part 4, we'll look more closely at attitudes and behavior.

The *Yoga Sūtras* presents an eightfold path to self-knowledge, clarity, and freedom. This path is known as the "Eight Limbs of Yoga." The first two of the eight limbs are *yamas* and *niyamas*. At first glance, *yamas* and *niyamas* appear to be a set of dos and don'ts. But as originally presented, they were descriptions of—rather than prescriptions for—attitudes and behaviors of those who had attained enlightenment. The *yamas* and *niyamas* offer an inner and outer portrait of a fully realized person, as if to say, "This is how an awakened person looks. This is how such a person behaves." From ancient times to the present, those on the path to transformation have reflected the same attitudes and behaviors described in the *yamas* and *niyamas*.

The *yamas* and *niyamas* are guides, rather than any moral code, set of precepts, or list of commandments that one must uphold. Most of us rebel when presented with a list of shoulds or musts. A list of dos and don'ts can lead us into following rules rigidly—which is yet another way to disturb, rather than calm, the mind.

The intention of *yamas* and *niyamas* is to bring awareness to our attitudes and behavior, and their effects on us. For example, when we explore *ahimsā* (non-harmfulness), we become more aware of ways in which we think and act unkindly. More importantly, we become aware of the effects on our minds from this way of thinking and behaving. We see that our harmful thinking or behavior creates disturbance in our minds. The link between *ahimsā* and our own peace of mind soon becomes clear. When we intentionally cultivate our own peace of mind, this practice naturally extends outward. There is no need to "try" to treat others more kindly, or to "be good for goodness' sake." In other words, our inner work benefits everything and everyone beyond us.

But, as Hariharananda Aranya and other commentators of the *Yoga Sūtras* emphasize, those seeking self-realization cannot first begin with the practice of *yamas/niyamas*. Instead, seekers are urged to undertake a Yoga practice (*āsana*, *prāṇāyāma*, and meditation) with the goal of attaining clarity. Over time, our Yoga practice (and especially meditation) reveals to us our harmful patterns of thought and behavior. This awareness causes us to move away from things that disturb our mind and toward things that promote peace of mind. In other words, as we continue to practice Yoga, we begin to embody the *yamas* and *niyamas*.

The yamas and niyamas are the most ancient form of cognitive behavioral therapy (CBT). CBT is a type of psychotherapy in which negative patterns of thought about the self and the world are challenged, in order to alter unwanted patterns of behavior. By reflecting on ourselves within the yamas and niyamas framework, we cultivate awareness of all our behavior patterns and attitudes, wanted and unwanted. This awareness is the first step toward cultivating new patterns more in line with the peace of mind that characterizes a person on the Yogic path.
The yamas and niyamas are:

Yamas

- ***ahimsā***—refraining from harm
- ***satya***—truthfulness
- ***asteya***—non-stealing
- ***brahmacarya***—respecting our senses
- ***aparigraha***—non-covetousness

Niyamas

- ***śauca***—cleanliness
- ***santoşa***—contentment
- ***tapas***—self-discipline
- ***svādhyāya***—self-inquiry
- ***iśvarapraṇidhāna***—surrendering the fruits of our actions

CHAPTER

15

Refraining from Harm (*Ahimsā*)

Ahimsā is characterized by compassion and friendliness toward every living being and thing in this world. The Sanskrit word *himsa* means "harm," and the prefix a means "not." Thus the literal English translation of *ahimsā* is "no harm." But the concept of *ahimsā* is more complex than this literal translation. *Ahimsā* means non-harmfulness in thought, word, and deed. Having *ahimsā* is not simply being the follower of a rule about not harming or hurting. It is a state of mind that lays a peaceful foundation for our interactions with the world and, most importantly, with ourselves.

Engaging in *ahimsā*, or non-harmfulness, is about examining our thoughts and behaviors, and avoiding those that cause disturbances in favor of those that create peace. A quiet Yoga practice encourages us to watch our angry thoughts and impulses, refrain from acting on them or identifying with them, and respond with clear-headed compassion. In terms of *ahimsā*, an ongoing practice of Yoga leads a person toward greater sensitivity to the sacredness of life, including, even, the lives of insects.

When we live with an attitude of compassion, our minds are more calm and steady. We stand up for ourselves when necessary, but we also resist breaking into anger or revenge, which can irritate our mental state.

I once experienced a period of beating myself up for not living up to the image of perfection that I had set for myself. As you can imagine, I was a very unhappy person at that time, pushing others away as I committed to my feeling of worthlessness. Thankfully, this happened to be the exact time I chose to be more serious about my Yoga practice. In my *āsana*, *prāṇāyāma*, and meditation practices I mustered the courage to examine my tendency to abuse myself and my body when I wasn't as perfect as I thought I could be. Slowly, as I grew and developed, my suffering began to reduce, but I first had to suffer the truth about myself, with honesty and compassion.

I envisioned myself talking with Mother Theresa, known throughout the world for touching people with her compassion. When I told her my thoughts about how I wasn't good enough, I imagined what she would say back to me. From that place, I began to embody *ahimsā* in a small way, which has grown since then and continues to grow for me.

Sadly, the world offers examples of himsa (harmfulness, injustice, violence) every day. List a few of these, from your own observations, for each category below.

4.15.1

- *Himsa* in words:____

- *Himsa* in images:____

- *Himsa* in actions:____

Compassion for our bodies. Our bodies can be victims of *himsa*-like thoughts. I've known many women and men who think and speak negatively about their bodies, comparing them to unrealistic expectations of how a body "should" look and perform. Some of us have even pushed our bodies beyond their limits until we became injured or ill, in the effort to reach some sort of ideal body.

Āsana practice encourages a sense of love and compassion toward our body. That means not treating our body as a separate entity to fight against. Instead, it is an amazing tool we use to experience the world.

EXERCISE 4.15.2

4.15.2

Perform the following sequence with an awareness of the amazing way your body can move and provide feedback to your brain. In this *āsana* practice, there is no need to strive for correction or perfection in the body or the breath. Simply be mindful of the various parts of your body that are engaged in the practice.

❶ Look at your hands with curiosity, as if you were looking at a stranger's hands. Bring them together and rub the palms back and forth softly. Notice the warmth and sound this creates.

❷ Interlace your fingers and press your palms outward. Then raise your arms slowly up and down three times. Feel the stretch in your hands, fingers, arms, and shoulders. You may let your gaze follow the movement of your hands if this is comfortable on your neck.

❸ Next, bend forward and place your hands on the floor, with your palms facing up, fingers pointing toward your feet. Bend your knees deeply, and step onto your hands. Move your toes around, feeling a massage in your palms. Hold this position for a moment, and then rise. Repeat one more time.

Continued on page 66

EXERCISE 4.15.2

4.15.2

❶

❷

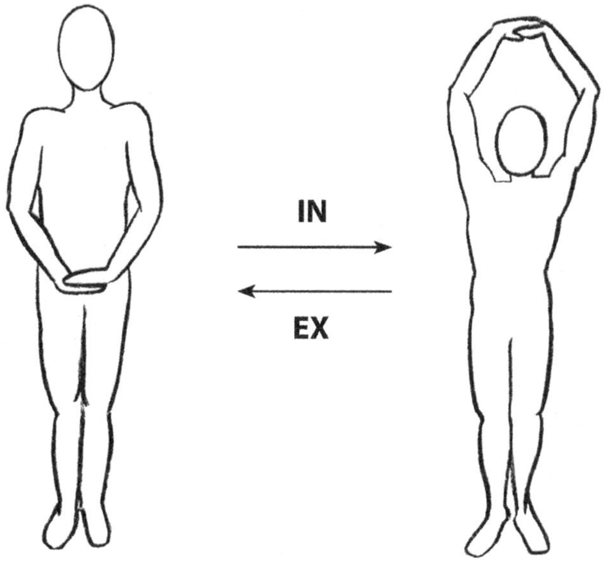

❸

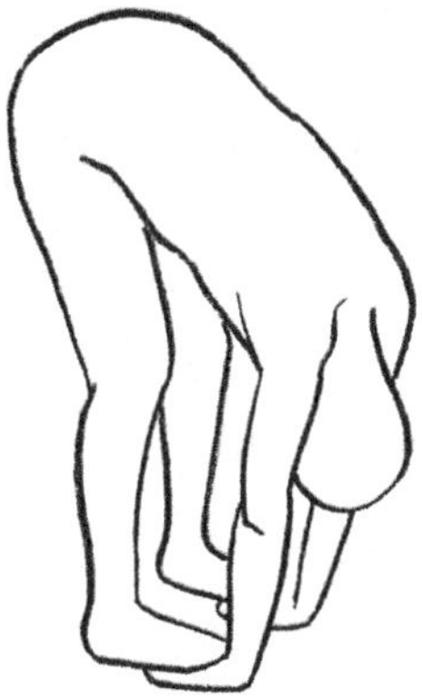

Continued on page 67

EXERCISE 4.15.2

4.15.2

❹ In the next portion of the sequence, you will move from a downward-facing dog posture to the plank position. Begin on your hands and knees. Flex your feet so that your toes bend forward, with your heels up. Then use the balls of your feet to lift your buttocks while pressing back with your hands to make your body form an inverted "V"—the shape of a dog or cat stretching after a nap. Lower your heels. (Your heels do not have to touch the floor unless you can do this comfortably.) From this position, lower your buttocks until you are in the plank position, which is the top position of a pushup, with arms and back straight. Next, you will flow from plank back to downward-facing dog. Repeat this sequence two more times. Sense your weight shifting from your legs and feet to your arms and hands as you move back and forth from downward-facing dog to plank posture.

❺ Lie on your back so you can begin to perform a reclining twist. Start with your arms extended from shoulder height, palms facing up. Bend the knees, bringing them toward your chest. Turn the knees to one side and lower them until they reach the floor. Hold for one breath. Focus on the sensation of the air touching your palms. Move the knees up and over to the other side, and again hold for one breath. Repeat once more on each side, this time focusing on the twisting sensations in the hips and back.

❻ Lying on your back, draw your knees toward your chest and place your hands on your knees. Then use your hands to gently and slowly push your knees away from your chest. Keeping your hands on your knees, exhale while drawing the knees in and inhale as you release them out. Repeat two more times. With eyes closed, be aware of your thoughts and bodily sensations as you repeat the movements.

4.15.2

In a nonjudgmental way, answer the following questions regarding exercises 1–6:

- Where and in what ways did your body communicate that it was limber or tight?____________

____

____

- Did your body communicate that it enjoyed one posture over another? If so, which ones? ____

____

____

- Briefly describe how it felt to observe your body with curiosity, rather than critically or with the attitude of performing a task. ________________________

____

- What was your state of mind before the *āsana*? After the *āsana* __________________

____

____

Continued

EXERCISE 4.15.2

4.15.2

❹

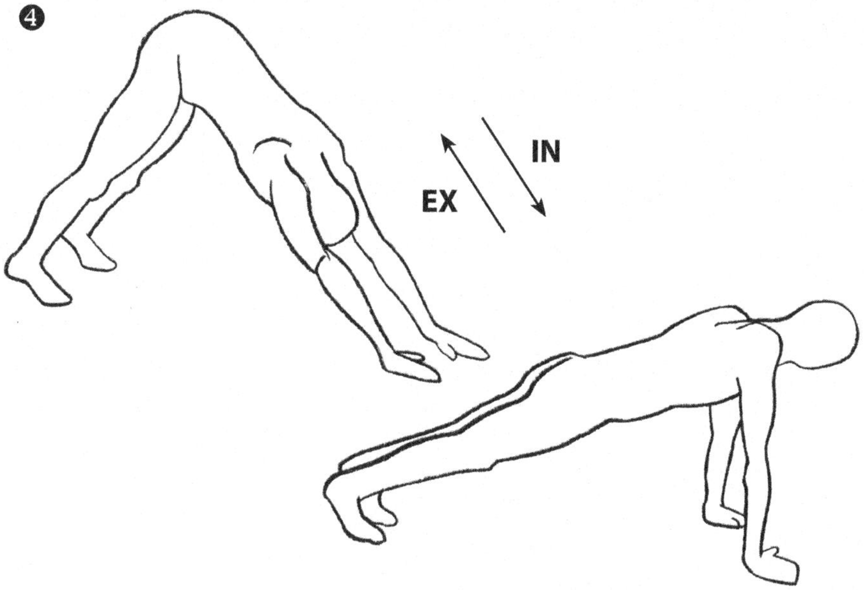

❺

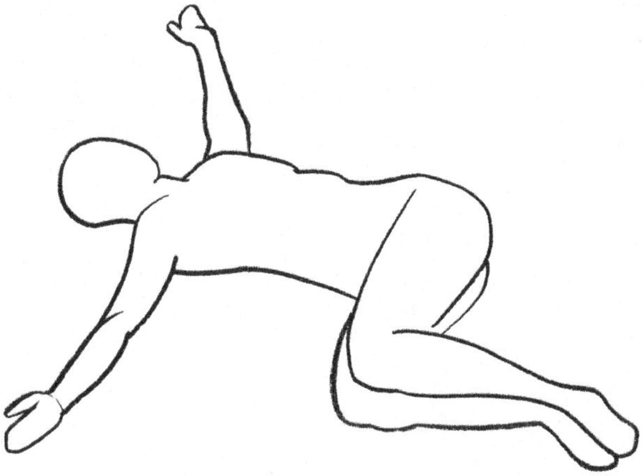

❻

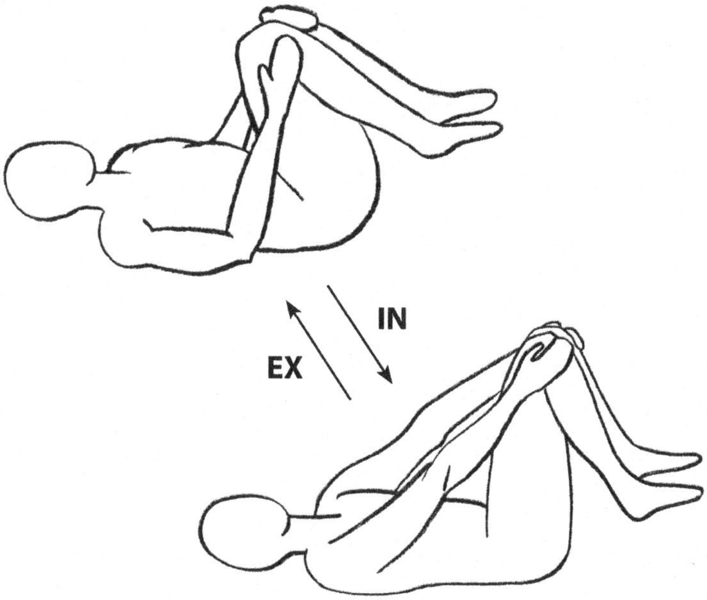

When you have an ongoing Yoga practice, you may find yourself behaving more warmly and friendly toward others. This, in turn, attracts and inspires others. The exact *sūtra* on this *yama* explains that when *ahimsā* is fully attained in a person, all people, even ones with negative intentions, will be moved toward compassion in that person's presence.

Emotions and breath. When we cultivate *ahimsā*, negative emotions that can overpower us are subdued. This is helpful because emotions like fear, anger, and sadness can affect our breath. For example, when we cry, the breath is ragged and short; when we yell in anger, we become breathless; when we are anxious or fearful, we hold the breath. When our breathing is altered in these ways, our sympathetic nervous system tells the rest of our body to be on high alert. Being on high alert throughout our day is taxing to our body and mind. In the Yoga practice of *prāṇāyāma* we learn to regulate our breathing. By gently calming and lengthening the breath, we stimulate our parasympathetic nervous system. That's the system that informs our body to rest, restore, and renew itself. Let's use the breath to cultivate a sense of *ahimsā* in this next exercise.

4.15.3

Imagine that you are trying to soothe a baby. Soften your face as well as your tone of voice. Even though you will be saying words mentally, you may whisper them if you choose. Sit or lie comfortably. Set a timer for 5 minutes, or plan on a few minutes for the exercise.

Find your normal resting breath, and attempt to lengthen the inhale and exhale by just one or two seconds.

1. With the inhale, mentally say, "May my *body* be—"
2. With the exhale, mentally say, "—at ease."
3. With the inhale, mentally say, "May my *mind* be—"
4. With the exhale, mentally say, "—at ease."
5. With the inhale, mentally say, "May my *breath* be—"
6. With the exhale, mentally say, "—at ease."
7. With the inhale, mentally say, "May my *life* be—"
8. With the exhale, mentally say, "—at ease."

Continue for the remaining time.

After the breathing exercise, answer this question:

What are some ways that I can bring a greater sense of ease into my life?

Responding to unkindness. *Himsa* (harmfulness) often arises in us when we feel attacked by someone else. We're often tempted to respond in kind, with harsh words or violent behavior, as if this will make them feel remorse and cause them to apologize for hurting us. But does responding in this way really work? It may make matters worse by triggering a heightened state of irritation.

Choosing an agitated mental state over a calm mental state is an example of *himsa* toward ourselves and others. And it's always possible that we have misinterpreted a remark as intentionally hurtful or misread a situation as deliberately harmful when that wasn't the case at all.

What happens in your mind when you feel that someone has been unkind to you? I have known the most mild-mannered people to become aggressive and hostile when behind the wheel of a car. For example, sometimes when another driver veers into my lane, my mind suddenly goes from a focused and clear mode to a high-alert mode. I feel threatened. I try to find the best way to defend myself or return the unkindness, or both. I'm on defense and offense at the same time.

4.15.4

Think about a time when your anger was suddenly triggered. Explore your feelings and actions by answering the questions below.

- What event triggered your anger or made you upset?____________________

- How much time passed before you recognized that you were upset?____________________

- What thoughts passed through your mind at first? ____________________

- What action or actions did you take based on the thoughts?____________________

- In hindsight, do you think your actions were reasonable? Explain ____________________

- What are some ways to create space between your thoughts and your actions when you find yourself feeling angry, hurt, or defensive? ____________________

Self-criticism. Harsh self-criticism is another form of *himsa*. Calling ourselves names, pointing out our failures, and engaging in the type of negative speech that we would never use with another person— these are all forms of abuse.

When we make a habit of this sort of self-criticism, it comes to feel normal—a default way of seeing ourselves. At deeper levels, self-criticism is a form of self-preoccupation and even pride, as in, "I'm too special to have ordinary expectations for myself; I must measure up to far higher standards than those of ordinary mortals!"

4.15.5 For one or more days, observe your mind's Critic. Make note of the circumstances and content of the self-criticism.

- Circumstance(s):____________________

- Content: ____________________

Use the space below to include additional circumstances and critical content during your observations of your inner Critic.

In my experience the following rhyme is not true.

Sticks and stones may break my bones
But names will never hurt me.

Repeated name-calling *does* hurt…especially if it is self-inflicted. In the cycle of negative thinking, one thought usually brings up a related thought. If I wake up on the wrong side of the bed and everything feels like a grind as I go through the day, a single negative self-criticism can multiply like a virus. Days like that make positive thinking and gratefulness hard practices to maintain.

I have taught many of my clients to use the word *ahimsā* out loud as a walking mantra to interrupt their self-deprecating cycle. Saying *ahimsā* helps them recall how good they feel during their Yoga practices and in my peaceful studio. It helps them return to their Yogic path.

4.15.6

Use *ahimsā* as a verbal tool by stating it out loud each time a self-deprecating thought arises. Shout it out if you have to! Use this powerful word as a compassionate means to blow the negative thoughts out of the ballpark.

- Briefly describe a situation in which you used the word *ahimsā* as a tool to override self-deprecating thoughts:____

- What was your experience during and after using the word *ahimsā* in this way? ____________

The attitude and practice of *ahimsā* is foundational in Yoga. A person who practices or embodies *ahimsā* is by that virtue practicing the other *yamas* and *niyamas*. For example, she is not lying, stealing, or desiring more material goods, because these are harmful to her peace of mind and to the peace of mind of others. When you walk through each day with a conscious intention to do no harm, you begin to see how expansive *ahimsā* can be.

CHAPTER

16

Truthfulness (*Satya*)

Satya means "truthfulness." With regard to our words, *satya* means to speak the truth in a way that promotes the well-being of others. It does not include speaking truths that cause harm (himsa) or lying to please others. With regard to our actions, *satya* means avoiding false communication through gestures or expressions.

With regard to our mind, *satya* means being aware of areas in which we lack integrity. *Satya* presupposes *ahimsā*. Recall from Chapter 15 some of the practices that lead us to *ahimsā*, thereby creating more peace of mind. In contrast, *himsa* creates disturbance. Thus, if we speak an uncompassionate truth, we let go of the most important *yama*, and our mind becomes agitated and less clear.

The truth according to me. Let's take a moment to review the subjective nature of truth. We often harm ourselves or others by believing that our stories are true (*viparyaya*). Our truths about someone or something aren't necessarily true—in fact they're rarely true in any objective way. This fact shows up most clearly in intimate relationships, in which our self-centered point of view often leads to "truths" such as: "You never listen to me," or "You're always so negative," or perhaps "You don't care about my feelings," and so on.

The issue in these cases is not how to constructively and compassionately tell the truth, but how to examine our stories to discover whether they're true. We can ask questions such as these, borrowed from Byron Katie's *The Work: "Is this thought true? Can I absolutely know that it's true? How do I react when I have that thought? Who would I be without that thought?"* We can avoid *himsa* by resisting the urge to believe in the absolute "truth" of our stories.

In the next two exercises, let's explore ways in which "truth"-telling can harm both ourselves and others.

4.16.1

Recall a time when someone else's truth hurt your feelings or made you angry.

- Briefly describe the situation:______________________________

  ____

- Summarize what this person said and the tone in which it was said: ______________________________

  ____

- What physical sensations do you associate with the issue?______________________________

  ____

- Do you think there is any truth in what the person said? Why or why not ______________________________

  ____

- What is one way the situation could have had a better result for both you and the other person? ______________________________

  ____

4.16.2

Recall a time when you felt it necessary to tell a difficult truth to someone.

- Describe your truth, as you saw it: ____
____
____
- On what basis did you believe this to be true?____
____
____
- How did you present your truth to the other person?____
____
____
- How did the person react to hearing your truth?____
____
- Looking back, is there anything you would have done differently in that situation? Explain. __
____
____
____

Speaking a supposed truth can backfire unless *ahimsā* is also present. We must consider the impact of our words prior to speaking. If, in telling the truth, we risk hurting others, it is better to keep quiet.

Have you ever begun a "truth-telling" statement with, "I'm sorry to tell you this, but . . ."? Sometimes we try to atone for what we're about to say before saying it, in order to soften the blow. It's as if we know in advance how the other person will react to what we're about to tell them. Or, less generously, we're trying to protect ourselves from the other person's negative reaction. In any case, it's helpful to take a moment to examine our motives when we're tempted to apologize in advance for telling what we believe to be the truth.

Satya and commitments. *Asatya* (untruth) is at the root of making commitments we don't really want to make. I have sometimes found myself saying "yes" to others because I wanted to please them. But, in truth, I wanted to say "no." The part of me that has been conditioned to please others sometimes sabotages my integrity. When we think that saying "no" is a bad thing to say, this can lead to lying and resentment.

My practice of Yoga has increased my sense of self-worth. I am better able to set boundaries and feel more comfortable speaking my truth in appropriate ways. Saying an honest "no" to commitments we cannot fulfill doesn't inherently mean that we are practicing *himsa*. In fact, it is the opposite. Saying a dishonest "yes" to commitments and tasks we cannot uphold is *himsa*. It creates an expectation in others, devalues our time, and often results in self-recrimination.

4.16.3

Recall a time when you said a dishonest "yes" to a task or commitment.

- Describe the situation:
- What led you to say "yes" instead of "no"?
- Did you complete the task/commitment? Explain.
- What were the costs and benefits of saying "yes" in this situation?

4.16.4

Recall a time when you said an honest "no" to a task or other commitment.

- Describe the situation:
- What led you to say "no" instead of "yes"?
- What were the results of your saying "no"?
- What were the costs and benefits of being honest in this situation?

White lies. A "white lie" is an untruth about a small matter that, in our judgment, presents no harm to others. For example, we might tell a white lie to avoid attending a friend's party or to give false praise in order to make someone feel better about themselves. But a white lie is still a lie, and we can never be completely sure that no harm is being done by our dishonesty.

Satya includes refraining from telling white lies. This also includes refraining from stretching the truth to exaggerate our importance or our accomplishments, to avoid responsibility, or to gain an advantage over others.

4.16.5

Just for today, notice moments in which you are tempted to lie, or actually do lie, in large or small ways. Include seemingly harmless white lies and truth stretching. Write about your observations.

- List situations in which you were tempted to lie, or did lie: ______________________

____

____

____

- In each case, what was your motivation for avoiding the truth? ______________________

____

____

____

- What happened as a result of lying or noticing the temptation to lie? ______________________

____

____

____

- Considering that everyone has lied, do you think there are situations in which it is acceptable, or even preferable, to lie? Explain. ______________________

____

____

____

____

You may have heard the saying "If you always tell the truth, you don't have to remember what you said." In essence, the more *satya* is embodied, the clearer the mind.

CHAPTER

17

Non-stealing (*Asteya*)

The English translation of *asteya* is "non-stealing." This means not taking physical nor intellectual property that doesn't belong to us, as well as refraining from coveting others' wealth or situation. Most of us refrain from taking our neighbors' belongings, but we may harbor jealousy over what our neighbors have. As we reflect on *asteya*, we will investigate our reactions to having something of ours taken without our permission. We will also explore our attitudes towards others' wealth, ideas, time, and more. Once again, we see that *ahimsā* is indirectly practiced when *asteya* is present.

4.17.1 Recall a situation in which something tangible of yours has been taken without your permission. Then recall a situation, if any, in which something intangible was taken without your permission.

- What *tangible* property was stolen from you? ______
- What were the circumstances of the theft? ______
- Describe your response to this experience: ______
- What *intangible* thing was stolen from you? ______
- What were the circumstances of the theft? ______
- Describe your response to this experience: ______
- Could you have prevented these thefts? If so, explain: ______

Now, let's investigate what happens when we practice *steya* ("stealing"). If you've ever taken something that didn't belong to you, you're familiar with the consequences, even if you didn't get caught. When I was twelve, I was on a field trip with my gymnastics team. Because I wanted to fit in with the older kids who were stealing postcards from the hotel lobby, I snuck out of my room, took a few postcards, and rushed back to the room to hide the postcards deep in my suitcase. That night, I felt so much guilt and remorse that I couldn't sleep. I kept waiting for the inevitable knock on the door from the police. My body was shivering with fear! Early the next morning, when everyone was still asleep, I snuck back into the hotel lobby and replaced the postcards on the rack. Years later, when I studied the Yoga *Sūtras*, I learned that mental distress can result in a shakiness of the body. The Sanskrit word for this is *aṅgamejayatva*: *aṅga* ="limbs"; *mejayatva* = "trembling."

Recall a situation in which you took something that did not belong to you.

4.17.2

- What did you take without permission?______________________________

____

____

- Describe the situation:______________________________

____

____

- Describe your feelings before and after the incident:______________________________

____

____

- Did you return what you took, or otherwise make amends for the theft? Explain. __________

____

____

- Looking back, describe any remaining feelings or thoughts about the incident(s) __________

____

____

Intellectual property. Intellectual property consists of ideas, inventions, songs, stories, websites, and so on. To some, the theft of intellectual property may appear more subtle or even permissible than the theft of tangible property, but the consequences of both are the same.

Gossip as steya. Gossip—taking the true or untrue information about another person's life and discussing it freely with others, without that person's permission—is *steya*. Therefore, it is also a form of *himsa*.

We sometimes discuss others' situations or behavior out of their presence, as a way to brainstorm ways to help them. More often than not, though, we discuss the lives of others just to share juicy details with friends and colleagues. Gossip offers a way to feel superior to our fellow humans.

While we can't stop other people from indulging in gossip, we can practice *asteya* by refraining from sharing others' personal information and by refusing to listen to gossip.

4.17.3 Recall one or more situations in which you were exposed to gossip about others, or were the subject of gossip yourself.

- Describe the things said about the other person, or about you:____________________

- To your knowledge, were these statements true or untrue? Explain____________________

- Describe your thoughts and feelings in connection with the gossip:____________________

The *Yoga Sūtras* state that when *asteya* is firmly established, one will receive the most valuable of all jewels—not literal jewels, of course, but the jewels of peace and contentment.

Theft of time. Another form of stealing is the theft of time—ours or someone else's. In many cases, we have the power to protect our time. For example, we can refuse to accept unwanted phone solicitations. We can walk away from conversations or activities that threaten our peace of mind or that are keeping us from more important tasks.

We can also misuse our own precious time by inventing ways to avoid a necessary task—for example, by mindlessly surfing the Internet instead of writing the report that is due or by browsing through a catalogue instead of returning the call of a friend in need.

If you've ever been on a silent retreat and then returned to regular life, you're aware of the great cloud of chatter that surrounds us much of the time. Some of the chatter seems harmless. It can be a nonthreatening way to interact with someone. But a great deal of chatter can be pointless and is not so much communication as noise.

Not everything we say must be profound and meaningful. Small talk has its value among friends, family members, coworkers, and others. However, if we view our speaking in terms of *asteya*, perhaps we will be more mindful and therefore more restrained in our speech—not overindulging in idle chatter, not giving voice to every thought that crosses our mind, and not wasting our time and others' time.

Consider ways that time can be stolen and ways to avoid stealing time in your life.

4.17.4

- List some activities or tasks that you consider a good use of time:______________________

____

____

____

- List some activities or tasks that you consider a theft of your time: ____________________

____

____

____

- Jot down some of your thoughts on the issue of theft of time:________________________

____

____

____

____

One good use of time is to do a Yoga practice or one aspect of it, such as *prāṇāyāma*. For a few moments today, practice *prāṇāyāma* in this way:

4.17.5

1. Focus on the natural pause at the top of your inhale.
2. Then focus on the still quality of the pause after your exhale.

Be mindful of the natural pauses in your breath, without influencing the length of the pauses.

Write about any feelings or sensations that arise within the pauses during *prāṇāyāma*.

____

____

____

____

____

____

____

____

____

CHAPTER

18 Respecting Our Senses (*Brahmacarya*)

Brahmacarya refers to controlling our sexual urges. Sex is addressed as a separate *yama* because it is one of our most powerful urges and includes all five senses and our sexual organs. In classical texts *brahmacarya* literally means "celibacy," but this practice is not intended for most of us. Rather, it is for a person such as a monk or a nun who is on the fulltime path to self-realization. Such a person must avoid any distraction from his or her path.

The modern interpretation of *brahmacarya* is "moderation regarding sexual conduct." This includes control over our thoughts about sexual matters, the amount and content of sexual images we view, our actions regarding sex, and other ways that we approach sex. The purpose of this type of restraint is to steady the mind.

Derailed by the senses. Sexual desire is normal in humans, but there are times when it can disrupt our clarity of mind. I remember when I made a decision to begin an exclusive romantic relationship. I felt sure about my choice and excited about the future with this person. Within one day of making this commitment, three attractive men approached me for a date. Talk about disrupted clarity! I suddenly began to question my original choice. Did I choose the right person? Did I make my decision too quickly? Would I be bored with just this one person for the rest of my life? I desired all four persons, sexually and in other ways. My clear choice suddenly seemed muddy.

Because of the potential for us to become captive to any of our senses, we can expand the definition of *brahmacarya* to include control over all our senses, not just our sexual urges. For example, if we are committed to eating a healthful diet and find ourselves facing a buffet table filled with tantalizing fat- and sugar-laden foods, we can embody *brahmacarya* by steering ourselves away from the table.

4.18.1 Think of a time when you made a decision or commitment under the influence of your senses—including sexual desire, if applicable—only to have it threatened or derailed by competing desires.

- Describe your experience:______________________________

- What was pleasant about the experience? What was unpleasant about it? ______________________________

- Which of your senses seem to have more power over your actions? Explain______________________________

Human sexuality. We are sensual beings. Within humans and other animals there is a primordial instinct to procreate, and that instinct is expressed in sexual desire. We are free to choose whether to bear children, but the instinct is there, regardless. For some animals, sexual desire is subdued until hormones push them to go into heat in order for their species to survive. For humans, on the other hand, our sexual desire is more perennial—and in our modern world is even encouraged. Let's explore some of the ways that our culture promotes sexual desire.

4.18.2

Observe ways that human sexuality is addressed through TV, movies, the Internet, magazines, and through people you come into contact with. Write examples of the various messages about human sexuality you notice.

- Television:____________________
- Movies:____________________
- Internet:____________________
- Magazines:____________________
- Other sources:____________________

No matter our age or relationship status, our minds and senses can be inspired and even hijacked when we encounter someone attractive. Let's explore these occasions in the exercise below.

4.18.3

Observe and then write about ways that you respond when you encounter a person who is sexually attractive.

- What physical changes in yourself do you notice in this situation?____________________
- What emotional and behavioral changes do you notice?____________________
- What changes do you notice in your thinking?____________________

The other five senses. As mentioned previously, *brahmacarya* can include moderation in all senses. Our senses help us experience the world, but when we overdo it, our mind becomes unsettled. For example, when we see extreme violence or exploitive sex on television or in a movie, our mind becomes agitated, be it with excitement, anger, fear, or revulsion. The same can be true when we listen to radio news or music, or when our sense of smell is overburdened by noxious fumes. As we will discuss in Chapter 20, what we allow our mouths to taste (especially alcohol, sugar, and fried foods) has a large impact on our state of mind.

EXERCISE

4.18.4

Let's bring the idea of moderation of sight and hearing into our *āsana* practice. To moderate any of our senses, we first need to be aware of their nature. Do the following postures in a quiet room, free of distractions. Don't analyze or judge. Just observe.

❶ Focus your eyes on a single point ahead of you while you move slowly up and down on the balls of your feet. Move through these slow, controlled heel raises for four to six repetitions. Notice whether your eyes want to wander from their focal point.

❷ Stand with the feet shoulder-width apart. Inhale, raising the arms out to the side, exhale and bend to the right side while taking your gaze upward to the left middle finger. Inhale and return to standing with the arms outstretched. Next, exhale and bend to the left side while taking your gaze up to the right middle finger. Then inhale and return to standing with arms outstretched. Exhale and lower your arms. Repeat this sequence four to six times, taking care not to overextend your neck. Notice the shifting of your sight from hand to hand—for example, notice the intensity of your gaze and the natural inclination to blink.

❸ Lie on your back for hip lifts. Inhale, pressing your feet into the floor while lifting your hips. Keeping your hips up, exhale, while gazing at your chest. Then, still keeping your hips up, inhale, observing your chest as you fill it with air. Finally, exhale while slowly bringing your hips down. Continue for three repetitions focusing on watching your chest expand and contract.

❹ Lie on your stomach with your head turned to one side and your arms at your sides. Focus your attention on sounds in the room, including the sound of your breathing.

Describe your experiences as you observed one or more senses during the *āsana* practice ______________________________

____

____

____

EXERCISE

4.18.4

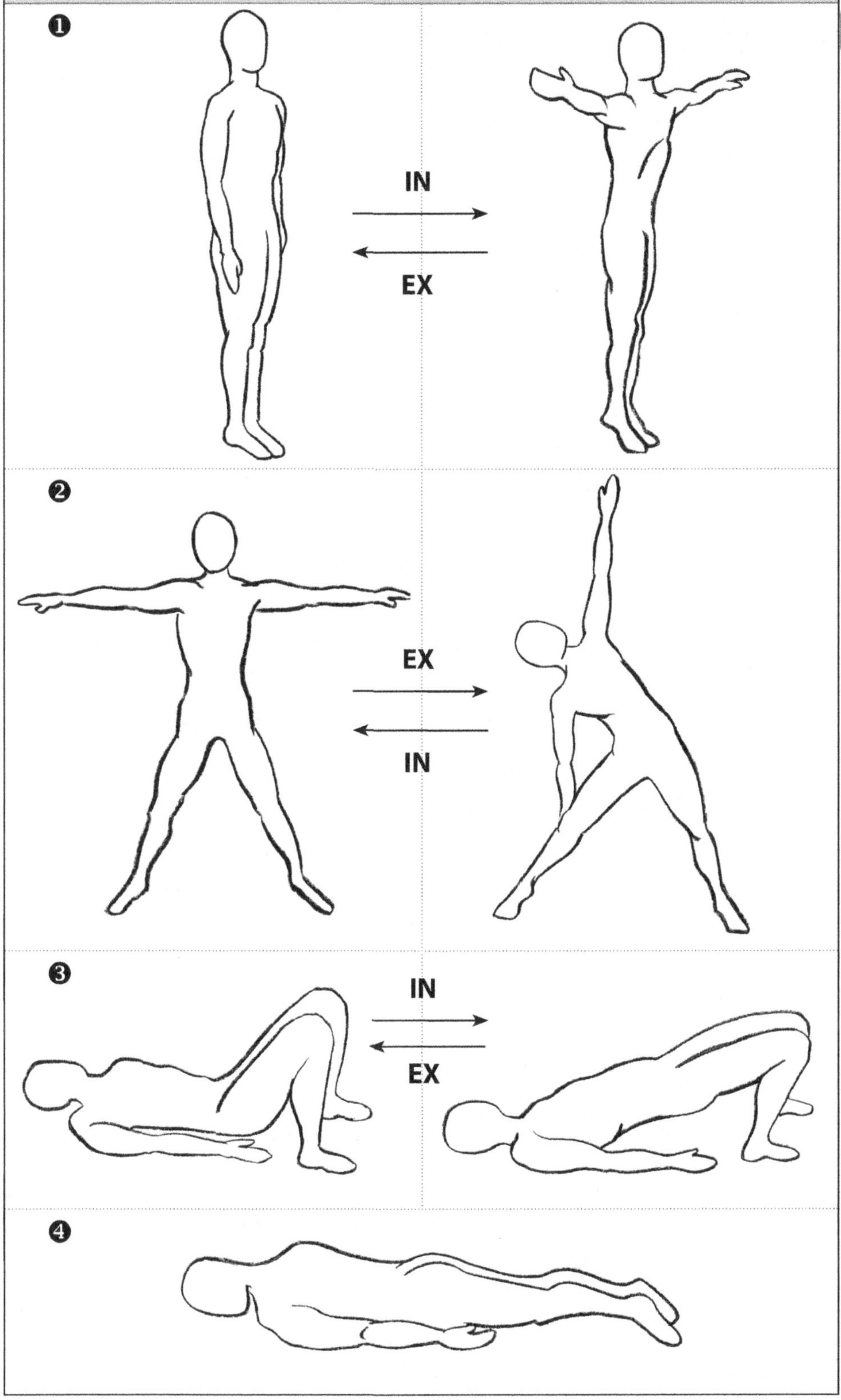

In addition to practicing Yoga as a way to modulate sensory overload, we can use nature to calm ourselves. Just looking at a tree outside a window can be restorative. So can sitting near water, taking a hike, or watching birds at a bird feeder. American naturalist and essayist John Burroughs expressed this beautifully when he wrote the following:

> *I go to nature to be soothed and healed, and to have my senses put in order.*

CHAPTER

19

Non-Covetousness (*Aparigraha*)

In the Sankrit word *aparigraha*, a means "not," *pari* means "all around," and *graha* means "coveting or grasping." When we practice *aparigraha*, we see our wants with objectivity and are able to control them.

Buying something we've been wanting can feel great. There is excitement during and after the purchase. That excitement influences the mind to desire the experience again. (We explored this in the *rāga kleśa* in Chapter 12.) So we buy something else, and we acquire more and more. We may not need some of these things, and some may even bring us new problems. But we're tempted to keep repeating the experience.

Do we have too much stuff? Look at all the storage companies that people pay to store the things they can't fit into their homes. The more we acquire, be it money or possessions, the more our minds are occupied with the upkeep and protection of these things. This leads us away from, not toward, a mind filled with peace.

We live in a society that continually tells us that having money will bring us happiness. No doubt, having money can bring a certain ease in everyday living, but even an abundance of it cannot fix any of our personal problems. Just ask a lottery winner!

Aparigraha does not mean refraining from owning material goods. For example, a musician may legitimately need twenty guitars. It's the continual grasping for more and more goods that distracts our minds from peace.

Yoga teaches that the search for happiness in material objects is futile. This is because the objects will decay, break, or lose value over time. And our perspectives about objects (and even people) change over time. In a world where everything outside of us is always changing, it is impossible to find a solid object that will create or ensure our everlasting happiness. That can only come from within.

Material goods. In the 1979 movie *The Jerk*, Steve Martin's character, Navin, has lost everything, and now his wife, Marie, has ordered him to leave. Navin tries to shrug off his bad luck by insisting to Marie that he doesn't need anything or anyone . . . "except for this ashtray . . . and this paddle game . . . and this remote control . . . and . . .," he declares, as he randomly snatches up objects around the house. This scene from *The Jerk* illustrates our materialistic culture—how we're encouraged to "need" all sorts of material goods and how hard it is to let go of them.

4.19.1

Conduct an informal inventory of your material goods. For example, open a closet or a set of drawers, or survey the items in your garage, if you have one. Assess the objects in a single room, perhaps. List some items that you feel you *must have*, items that you could do without, and items about which you're undecided.

- Must-haveitems:____

- Unnecessaryitems:____

- Not-sure items: ____

Maintaining and protecting material possessions and wealth takes time and attention. First, our mind can become ensnared in deciding *which* thing to buy. Then we can become identified with an object we buy, as in, "*Now* people will respect me because of the car I drive." Next, we can be seized by the fear that our object might be stolen. Instead of owning objects, they can come to own us. In Yogic terms, the fewer things you own, the freer you are.

Letting go. We can take the practice of *aparigraha* a step further by applying it to letting go—especially of ideas and things we cling to unnecessarily. While we'd like to think that our reliable car or our satisfying relationship will stay the same forever, the world and everything we know of it is impermanent. In the practice of Yoga, we work on understanding that letting go is the natural way of things. This makes it easier to accept changes in life. Change is not inherently good or bad. It just happens.

In our Yoga practice, we try to avoid getting attached to a scheduled plan, a personal routine (except for a Yoga practice), or even a favorite dish at a restaurant. Rather than becoming disturbed because our plan, routine, or restaurant menu has changed, we strive to accept changes, let go, and move on.

We may not be able to practice absolute nonattachment, but we can see the benefits of being aware of our attachments and noticing our reluctance to let go of them. There's no need to let go of *everything*, like the Buddha, but we must cultivate the *willingness* to let go of habitual thought patterns and material things that create problems in our lives. *Peace is what remains if you let go.*

EXERCISE 4.19.2

4.19.2

You can infuse all aspects of your Yoga practice with an attitude of *letting go.* There is even a mantra you can say aloud (or silently) on each exhale during *āsana* or *prāṇāyāma*: *Om namaha* ("ohm nah mah hah"), which according to one translation means "I let go." Find a quiet place, free of interruptions, to practice *uttanāsana* (a standing forward bend described below) as a symbolic gesture of surrender or letting go.

❶ Stand solidly but relaxed, with your hands at your sides.

❷ Using *ujjayi* breathing, begin an inhale. A couple of seconds after beginning the inhale, slowly begin raising both arms in front of you. When the arms are completely raised, finish your inhale.

❸ Begin your exhale, gently drawing in the stomach muscles. A couple of seconds after beginning the exhale, slowly bend from the hips, reaching both arms, forward, out, and down toward your toes. Say *Om namaha* (aloud or silently) as you bend forward and down as far as you can comfortably go.

❹ When you have completed the exhale, begin the inhale, and then begin raising your arms and coming back to a standing position with the arms raised.

❺ Exhale and lower your arms to your sides. Repeat the forward bend several more times.

How did you feel as you practiced the *āsana* with an attitude of letting go?

Accumulating material goods leads to the desire for more material goods. Surely this is not the path to peace of mind. Accumulating peaceful experiences leads to the desire for more peaceful experiences. This is a treasure worth far more than any material object.

EXERCISE 4.19.2

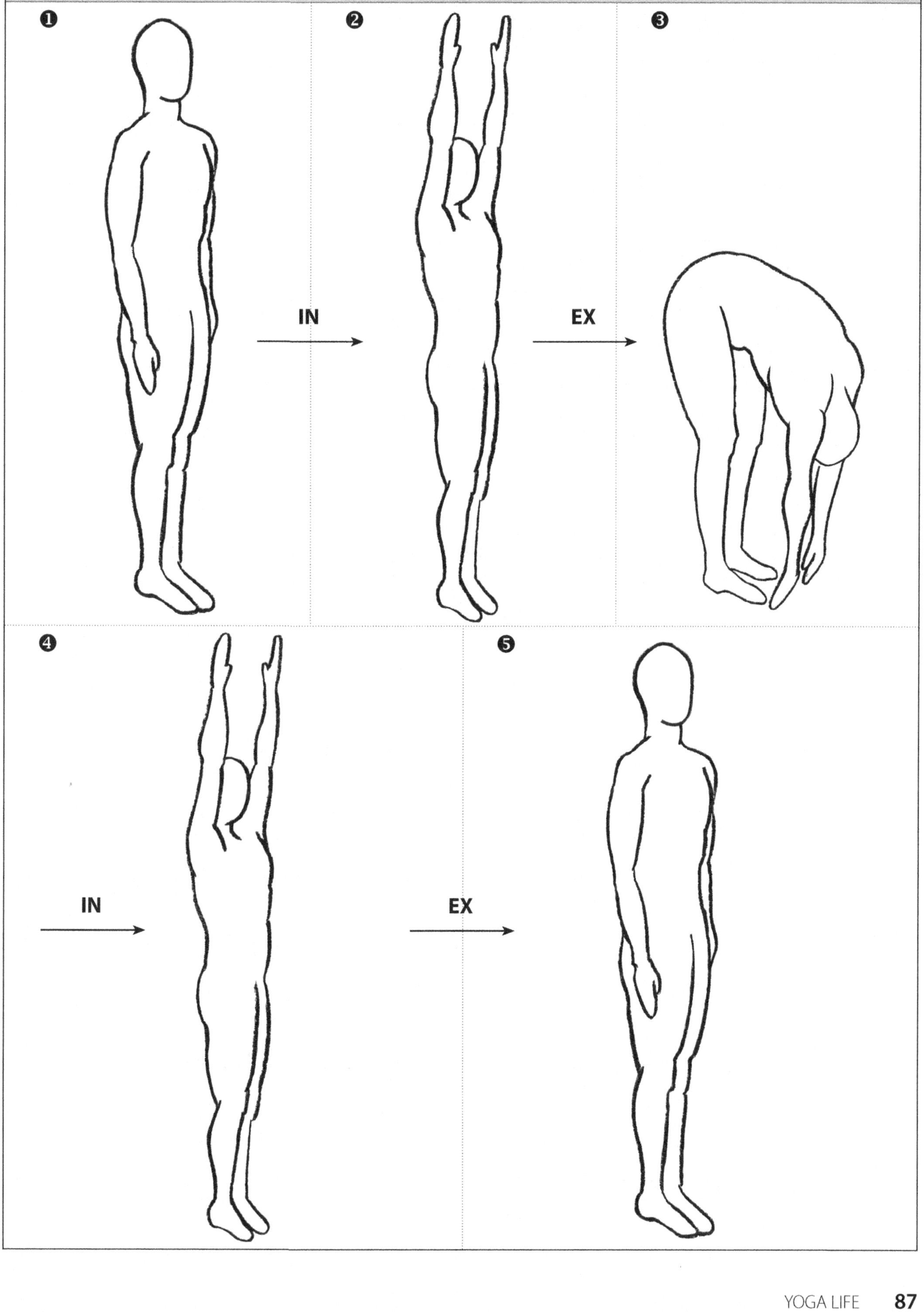

CHAPTER

20

Cleanliness (*Śauca*)

Śauca is the concept of keeping everything that is in our control clean and efficient. The literal English translation of *śauca* is "purity." *Śauca* applies to both outward and inward purity.

Outward *śauca* means maintaining an organized, clean, and clutter-free space. My studio is an oasis for me and for my clients. I maintain it in a way that promotes mental clarity and calm.

Inner *śauca* means eating and drinking items that promote easy digestion and keep us fueled with the energy we need. An even deeper sense of *śauca* concerns the mind. *Śauca* means keeping the mind free from arrogance, pride, malice, and so on. It also means not dwelling on disturbing thoughts or fantasies. This may require limiting what we take in from books, media outlets, performances, and other external sources.

Śauca can begin with keeping our home and workplace uncluttered so that there's minimal distraction for the senses. In a tidy home or workplace, we're less likely to lose things such as keys. This encourages a focused, calm, and clear mind.

4.20.1 Identify an area of your home or workplace that can be improved by de-cluttering or cleaning it. Set aside a time to clean and organize this area. After the task is finished, briefly describe how the area looked before you cleaned and organized it. Then briefly describe how it now looks. Finally, write about any mental effects of having done this task.

- Before cleaning/organizing:
- After cleaning/organizing:
- Mental effects:

Clean eating. *Śauca* applies also to noticing the effects of our food choices on our body and mind. Sometimes these effects are positive: a sense of vitality, having energy and stamina, and healthy skin, hair, and nails. Sometimes the effects are not positive: indigestion, nausea, bloating, allergic reactions, or more subtle effects such as a sense of tiredness or unease.

4.20.2

There is no uniform "best diet" that applies to all of us, but you probably have an idea of what foods and beverages are best for you, in the sense of bringing about a feeling of vitality and wellness. Plan a day in which you eat and drink in a way that you consider healthful. This may mean avoiding food additives, eating more fresh vegetables, or simply cooking your own meals. This is not an occasion for "doing a cleanse." Just eat and drink consciously for one day. Keep a record of what you eat and drink during the day. Then write about the mental and physical effects. Feel free to do this exercise for several days or several weeks, rather than just one day. Use a log such as the one below, allowing plenty of room to track all of your food and beverage choices and their effects each day.

- What I ate/drank: ______________________________

- Mental and physical effects: ______________________________

Inner cleanse. Another way to practice inner *śauca* is to "clean out" our lungs and minds through *prāṇāyāma*. Inhaling delivers much needed oxygen to our bodies while exhaling releases excess carbon dioxide. When done in particular ratios, *prāṇāyāma* can change our heart rate and blood pressure, and can even clear up light congestion and headaches. Similar to a healthy diet, our bodies like and sometimes crave a good *prāṇāyāma* practice.

4.20.3 Practice twelve rounds of breathing (an inhale and exhale is one round). You can do extended breathing, *ujjayi* breathing, or your normal breathing. With each inhale and exhale, feel the movement of your lungs, diaphragm, and abdomen. Try to picture in your mind their inner workings.

As we pay attention to the body while breathing, we bring *śauca* to our nervous system.

Minding the senses. Practicing *śauca* can further include cleanliness of mind by paying attention to what we consume with our eyes and ears. We explored this in Chapter 18. Sometimes what we hear on the radio, see on TV or on the Internet, or read in newspapers can be upsetting or even overstimulating. We can find ourselves dwelling on such things for days afterward.

Use the next exercise to observe the effects of avoiding sounds, images, or printed information that can disturb our mind.

4.20.4 Set aside one or more days to abstain from some or all of the following: radio, television, movies, the Internet, magazines, and newspapers. Write about the experience

- What media did you avoid during this time? ______________________

____

____

____

- Were any aspects of the exercise difficult? If so, describe these: ______________________

____

____

____

- What, if anything, surprised you about the exercise?______________________

____

____

____

- What did you notice about your mental state as you refrained from one or more of the media?

____

____

____

____

4.20.5

Let's use *prāṇāyāma* again as a tool to cleanse from within. *Uddīyāna-bandha* involves a complete exhale, with suspension of the breath, and a lifting of the abdominal wall. This *bandha* is best done on an empty stomach and, preferably, with empty bowels.

1. Inhale and then exhale completely.

2. Before you inhale again, hold the exhale (also called suspension of the breath). As you suspend the breath, use your abdominal muscles to lift your abdomen toward your sternum.

3. Try *uddīyāna-bandha* several times, taking resting breaths between each breath cycle. As you lift, there is a sensation of closing the throat with the tongue and a mock inhale to help you engage the internal muscles. This is an experiment on the *bandha*, not a relaxing *prāṇāyāma.*

Describe your experience with this *bandha*:______________________________

CHAPTER

21 Contentment (*Santoṣa*)

Santoṣa is most often translated in English as "contentment," as in the sense that everything we have in our lives right now is exactly what we need. It is an absence of the desire for more than is necessary to maintain our life and also an acceptance of what happens to us. This is not to say that all desire will be absent (refer to *Rāga* in Part 3), but in *santoṣa*, we look closely at our desires and investigate the expectations associated with them.

There is an inherent expectation in all our actions. When something doesn't go according to plan, we experience varying levels of disappointment, from minor to debilitating. *Santoṣa* means having a neutral expectation while pursuing our desires. It lessens the upset— for we become rooted in gratefulness for what we have, not focused completely on fulfilling our desires. That way, whether or not we get what we want, our mental state remains steady.

4.21.1 Consider whether what you currently have (for example, material goods, activities or practices, or relationships) is "enough." Then answer the questions below.

- What material goods are currently essential to your well-being?____________________

- What current activities or practices are essential to your well-being?____________________

- What current relationships are essential to your well-being? ____________________

- How would you describe your overall level of satisfaction with what you have in life?________

Being okay with *you*. Let's take a moment to reflect on acceptance and contentment with the self. This can apply to acceptance of our physical traits as well as acceptance of our habitual ways of thinking. In a culture in which images of male and female bodies are airbrushed to perfection, it can be hard not to compare those bodies with our own and feel critical of our bodies. Yoga is a spiritual path of transformation that comes from within. That transformation requires acceptance of where we are and a willingness to be content with what has been, what is now, and what will be.

4.21.2

Can you accept yourself as you are? Let's explore things about ourselves that we feel good about, things we wish were different, and ways that we feel grateful for both categories. As an example of the latter category, we may wish that our feet were smaller or our toes more attractive, but we could feel grateful for how faithfully they've supported our body all these years.

- What physical traits of yours do you feel good about? ____________________

____

____

____

- What physical traits of yours do you wish were different? ____________________

____

____

____

- What do you appreciate about these less-than-perfect aspects of your body? ____________________

____

____

____

Focusing on what we lack can sometimes motivate us to set and reach goals, but it can also create a constant feeling of discontent. Like Goldilocks, we have the potential to be *just right* anytime we want. Perhaps we don't have everything we desire, but with a closer look, we may find that we are actually living in abundance.

4.21.3

Let's conduct an "abundance inventory" of material and nonmaterial things in your life.

- List examples of material abundance in your life: ____________________

____

____

____

- List examples of nonmaterial abundance in your life: ____________________

____

____

Throughout your day, you may want to use the following as a walking mantra to bring *santoṣa* to your mind.

Inhale as you mentally recite "I have enough." Exhale as you mentally recite "I am enough."

"It isn't what you have, or who you are, or where you are, or what you are doing that makes you happy or unhappy. It is what you think about it."

~ Dale Carnegie

CHAPTER

22 Self-Discipline (*Tapas*)

Tapas is the mental attitude that allows us to endure the discomfort of creating change. The root word *tap* in *tapas* means "to heat." Essentially, *tapas* is the friction of discomfort we go through to replace unhealthful habits with healthful ones. It's akin to heating water in order to boil out impurities. Every stage of development in a person's life involves the pain of leaving something behind in order to move to the next level. Any changes, even positive changes, can be difficult.

Tapas is the primary component of *Kriyā Yoga* (the Yoga of Action). It is the first step on the spiritual path I describe in this workbook. Walking this path is not always easy. We will undergo trials and tribulations as we move toward peace. We may have to change unhelpful thought patterns that we have used for years.

4.22.1

Let's use this exercise to explore some of our healthful habits and unhealthful habits.

- List some of your healthful habits:______________________________

____
____
____
____

- List some of your unhealthful habits:______________________________

____
____
____
____

- What are some unhealthful habits you have changed or eliminated? ______________

____
____
____
____

- What are some unhealthful habits you have changed or eliminated? ______________

____
____
____
____

Enduring discomfort. We practice *tapas* when we endure discomfort in order to create a beneficial change in our lives. This is not to be confused with extreme measures such as fasting for ten days in order to lose a few pounds or to impress others. The willingness to endure the "heat" of *tapas* moves us towards clarity and peace in our minds, not toward accolades for feats of endurance.

4.22.2

To begin to understand *tapas,* we will use it to endure discomfort that arises while sitting still. Set a timer for 5 minutes. Sit completely still. Observe the process of settling your body. Do not try to control your mind. Let it do what it will, whether it is daydreaming, creating a list, reliving memories, and so on. If physical or mental discomfort arises, just note it but do not try to change anything.

When you finish the exercise, rate your overall level of discomfort during the experience. Circle the number that represents your level of discomfort, 0 being the least discomfort and 10 the greatest.

0------1------2-----3------4-----5-----6-----7-----8-----9-----10

- What, if any, unpleasant sensations did you experience, such as bodily discomfort, distractions, or resistance?______________________________

- What, if any, pleasant sensations did you experience during the exercise ________________

Suppose we're trying to avoid caffeine. Here's a "snapshot" of what happens as we try to resist the temptation to drink a caffeinated beverage.

1. The mind has a thought: *I want an afternoon pick-me-up!*
2. The senses respond: we imagine ourselves holding the drink, drinking it, enjoying it.
3. We either yield to the temptation or resist it.
4. We experience the consequences of yielding or resisting.

Our mind's tendency is to follow our senses rather than focus on the reasons to avoid caffeine. The senses want immediate satisfaction. They're not thinking about the benefits of avoiding caffeine. We are always free to indulge our senses for temporary satisfaction, but sooner or later we find that the temporary satisfactions aren't working for us. This leads us to look for ways to change or eliminate the habit in order to experience a deeper satisfaction.

4.22.3

Our resolve is tested daily (or even hourly!) when we are working on beneficial change. If we are trying to avoid sweets, our resolve is tested if a friend wants to meet at a bakery, and it is strengthened if we suggest meeting our friend for a walk instead. Let's explore things that support our efforts to make beneficial change and things that try to sabotage our efforts to change.

- What is an unhealthy habit you want to eliminate or change?______________________________

- What are some triggers that tempt you to engage in the unhealthy habit?_______________

- What are some things that help you resist the temptation to indulge in the unhealthy habit?

Saṁskāra. Some of our unhealthful habits are attempts to control stress in our lives. Sadly, stress doesn't magically disappear. To reduce it we often find short-term relief in various ways: mindlessly eating in front of the TV, drinking alcohol, playing video games, shopping, and so on. Such activities temporarily soothe the stress and help distract us from irritants in our lives.

But these can eventually become long-term avoidance habits. Instead of indulging in the occasional shopping venture, we *over*indulge to the point of maxing out our credit cards. That leads to money problems, which have emotional as well as financial consequences. The *fear* of not having enough money to pay the bills, the *anger* at yourself for creating the situation, and the *shame* in choosing the habit over and over again can cause you to go on another shopping spree to relieve the stress.

This mental loop is called a *saṁskāra*. When we're caught in a harmful *saṁskāra*, thoughts that lead to feelings of guilt, shame, frustration, and so on can make us feel powerless over our own minds. This is where *tapas* is useful. Through *tapas*, we learn to tolerate temporary unpleasant emotions, to remind ourselves that there is possibility of change for the better, and to break harmful mental loops by attempting different soothing techniques.

Active practices of Yoga are helpful in breaking free of harmful *saṁskāras*. Breath work (*prāṇāyāma*) can help cleanse the mind of the negative thought loop and bring us to a state of centered relaxation. It activates our parasympathetic nervous system, which is an innate soothing tool we have inside of us. Our heart rate and blood pressure become lower, and a general feeling of "okayness" overrides anxiety.

4.22.4 In this exercise, we will use the breath to stimulate our relaxation response in order to soothe discomfort associated with changes such as breaking an unwanted habit. The following alternate-nostril breathing practice is called: *nādīśodhana prāṇāyāma*. If you have not done this type of *prāṇāyāma* before, you may want to have a friend read the steps to you as you follow them. Refer to exercise 1.4.2 for correct hand positioning.

1. Find a quiet place to do the exercise.
2. Set a timer for 5 minutes.
3. Seat yourself comfortably, with an erect spine.
4. With your right hand, draw the index and middle finger toward the palm. That leaves the thumb, ring finger, and pinky extended.
5. Use the thumb of your right hand to draw downward on the right nostril with enough pressure to gently close the nostril. Simultaneously use the ring finger to halfway close the left nostril.
6. Inhale through the partially closed left nostril.
7. Before the exhale, use the ring finger to fully close the left nostril. Release pressure on the right nostril so that it is only partially closed.
8. Exhale through the partially closed right nostril.
9. Inhale through the partially closed right nostril, keeping the left nostril completely closed.
10. Before the exhale, release the pressure on the left nostril and fully close the right nostril.
11. Exhale through the partially closed left nostril.
12. Repeat this cycle until time is up. Feel free to extend the time of the exercise to further explore its results.

- What were your thoughts and feelings as you did this exercise?____________________

- Did you experience a sense of calm? Explain.____________________

Exercise 4.22.4 shows one way to bring peace to our minds and bodies. It demonstrates that we have an *active*, rather than passive, role in our Yoga practice. The next exercise also demonstrates how we can actively practice *tapas*.

4.22.5

Many of us habitually check our phones, computers, and watches for the latest message, email, or news. While this may not necessarily bring discord to our life, we can explore *tapas* by refraining from checking our phone, computer, and other electronic devices for a certain amount of time.

Practice *tapas* today by waiting to turn on any electronic device until your workday officially begins, or by turning off the device after your workday is done. Use the following discomfort scale to rate your experience, 0 being the least discomfort and 10 being the most.

0------1------2-----3------4-----5-----6-----7-----8-----9-----10

Note your thoughts and feelings during the exercise.

____

____

____

____

____

____

____

Maladapted regulatory system. When we're undergoing difficulties in our life, it's easy to opt for an immediate, short-term solution by using alcohol, food, video games, the Internet, and so on. But these are only temporary measures, and we soon find that the original problem reappears in our minds. These short-term solutions produce illusions of relief and happiness and postpone our looking within to enact real change in the way we respond to difficulties.

4.22.6

Just for today, be aware of any unhealthy coping mechanisms you use when confronted with a problem or a difficult situation. What superficial or unhealthy fixes do you use to soothe yourself?

- Problem or difficult situation: ______________________________

  ____

  ____

  ____

  ____

- Unhealthy fix to soothe myself: ______________________________

  ____

  ____

  ____

  ____

Atapas refers to indulging in behaviors that lead away from peace. For example, having an occasional cocktail with friends can be enjoyable. It can create pleasant memories and may even deepen our connection to others. But when we overdo it, the effects are not so pleasant—such as a headache, stomachache, disturbed sleep, and impaired focus the next day. If you have done as I have in the past, you know how terrible a hangover feels! However, you might engage in the same behavior again, even though you're aware of the consequences. This is *atapas*—indulging in an unhealthy behavior for pain avoidance or out of absent-mindedness, instead of pursuing peace.

It is vital to understand that when we indulge in *atapas* over and over, we are imprinting that unhealthy pattern deeper in our mind. The imprint starts to feel like a part of us, of who we are and how we behave. Thus, we do it again tomorrow because it is "what we do" to relax after work. The imprint becomes so deep that trying to stop the habit is a difficult struggle.

A mind more at peace is filled with healthy *saṁskāras*—ones that support all of the *yamas* and *niyamas*.

4.22.7 Today, observe the choices you make throughout the day. Notice any choices that you would consider *atapas*—ones that cultivate unhealthy *saṁskāras.*

- List some of your atapas choices:____________________

- How might you build healthier *saṁskāras?*____________________

Personal tapas is the friction of a healthy *saṁskāra* rubbing up against an unhealthy *saṁskāra*. The discomfort of this friction is necessary in order to create calm in our minds, just as a prescribed burn promotes forest health and protects native species.

CHAPTER

23 Self-Inquiry (*Svādhyāya*)

Svādhyāya comes from three Sanskrit words: sva, which means "self," adhi, which means "toward" or "based on," and *ayana*, which means "movement." In English, the literal meaning of *svādhyāya* is "to move nearer to the self" or "rooted in or based on one's self." The "self" in this context refers to something more than our physical being. Through *svādhyāya*, we discover that we are neither the body nor the mind alone. We come closer to knowing our authentic self.

Svādhyāya is approached in two different ways. One way is through reading a text such as the Yoga *Sūtras* as a reference point for self-reflection. Reading about the goal of peace and how to attain it reminds us of our path and influences our goals. Reading about *yamas* and *niyamas* causes us to reflect on and compare how our attitudes have changed and will continue to change throughout our journey. In fact, focusing on this workbook is *svādhyāya!* The exercises in this workbook offer a way to reflect upon your thinking and your behavior. Confucius said that reflection is the noblest way to gain wisdom.

The other approach to *svādhyāya* is through meditation on the self. This is embodied in all of the Yoga practices (*āsana*, *prāṇāyāma*, and meditation), whose goals are to quiet the active brain in order to experience a deeper sense of self. In Yoga, we call this deeper self the "authentic self"—the self that hasn't changed since our first breath. Our day-to-day self changes all the time! The things we like and those we dislike change. Our energy levels and moods change. But the authentic self is always neutral and unchanging. Our Yoga practice taps into our desire to connect with the self that is unchanging, peaceful, and content.

Svādhyāya is also defined in several texts as *mantra japa*. *Man* means "mind," tra means "protect," and *jap* means "repeat." The repetition of a mantra or prayer can be considered *svādhyāya* because when you are fully engaged in *mantra japa*, there is no room for other types of thought. The repetition can be done aloud or silently. Tokens such as mala beads or rosary beads can be used to provide structure and grounding in this type of meditation. When used often enough, such tokens can by themselves provoke a sense of peace and quiet in the mind.

4.23.1

Find or create a meditation token that is meaningful to you. Then set aside a few moments to sit quietly with the token in your hands. Gaze at the token and allow it to "speak" to you. Notice what, if anything, you project from within yourself onto the token. (If you find that the token has a variety of associations that might distract or disturb your mind, choose a more neutral token.)

Cultivate an association between the token and a feeling of steadiness and calmness. Then write about the experience.

- What token did you select?
- Why did you choose this particular token?
- What thoughts and feelings arose as you gazed at the token?
- Do you plan to use the token during a meditation practice? Explain.

4.23.2

Silently or aloud, recite "May I be at peace" for 5 minutes, or for the time it takes to move through the length of meditation beads, if you have them.

Now close your eyes and listen for sounds within your body.

Write about any feelings that arose before, during, and after this meditation

4.23.3

Svādhyāya involves engaging active Yoga practices (*āsana*, *prāṇāyāma*, meditation) to create a distance between our sense of *self* and our thoughts. This exercise attempts to link our thoughts with the sun. An exercise such as this cultivates the ability to consciously link our *self* with an entity that can provide us with energy, health, and peace. Let us bring the magnificence of the sun metaphorically into our beings. Recite the following poem aloud:

Even

After

All this time,

The Sun never says to the Earth,

"You owe me."

Look

What happens

With a love like that.

It lights the whole sky.

~Hafez

Go outside or to a sunlit window. Inhale, opening your arms wide as if to scoop up the energy from the sun. Exhale, bringing your hands to your chest as if to bring the sun's energy inside of you. As that begins to feel comfortable, recite silently, sing, or chant aloud "Thank you, Sun" when bringing the hands to your chest. Repeat for several minutes. The sun removes darkness with its glorious illumination. Choose to bring light and clarity to your body and mind.

- What were your thoughts and feelings as you began the exercise? ____________________

- What were your thoughts and feelings as you expressed thanks to the sun? ____________________

- What, if any, resistance did you feel during the exercise? ____________________

- What additional thoughts and feelings arose during or after the exercise? ____________________

"Yoga is your own inner self-help line." This quote is from A.G. Mohan, an inspiring Yoga teacher. It means that we can use Yoga to "dial in" to receive the help we are looking for.

Each of us is unique, so our search within will be unique as well. For example, two seekers in seated meditation may outwardly look the same, but what is happening in their minds will likely differ. Some of us may use a mantra, some may use visualization, some may meditate on the breath. In the past, the words in mantras were considered so important that they were selected by an experienced teacher, guide, or guru *specifically* for each student to ensure that the mantra would be effective for that particular student.

In other words, these teachers understood that one mantra, prayer, or saying would not be compelling for all students. Nowadays, the same mantra might be assigned to a roomful of students, without regard to individual differences. You may want to speak with your Yoga teacher or advisor to ensure that your current methods for finding focus and peace are appropriate to your particular temperament, needs, habits, and so on

As you access your "inner self-help line" through meditation or other practices, try not to get discouraged by the hyperactivity of the mind. Remember, thinking is the job of the mind. Attempting even a bit of meditation each day promotes the habit and can lessen resistance.

4.23.4 Before you go to bed tonight, use your mala beads or another counting instrument with the mantra "May I be at peace." Tomorrow morning, write about your experience.

Did the quiet repetition affect your sleep quality, dreams, or even waking thoughts? If so, in what way or ways?

4.23.5

In exercise 1.4.7, we used the Sanskrit word *śanti* ("peace"). We will use *śanti* again as a mantra *japa* practice following some movement. As you repeat *śanti* during the practice, let the word infuse you with a sense of calmness, softness, and peace.

1. Find a quiet place that is free of interruption.
2. Prepare for meditation by moving your body in a gentle *āsana* sequence, such as one forward bend, one side bend on each side, and one balancing posture for about two minutes. This is your time to move your body in any way you prefer, which is why this posture practice isn't specific. If you do need something specific, please refer to the first three steps in exercise 4.15.2.
3. Set a timer for 4 minutes.
4. Sit comfortably and begin your meditation, repeating *śanti* aloud during the 4 minutes. If your mind wanders, gently bring it back by focusing on the sound of *śanti*, as well as on the sensation in your mouth and lips as you repeat the mantra.
5. When time is up, remain seated or move to a lying position for another minute or two. Then write about your experience.

How did you feel—physically and mentally—during the beginning, middle, and end of the meditation?

- Beginning: ____
- Middle: ____
- End: ____

Was *śanti* effective as a mantra for you? Explain. ____

CHAPTER

24

Surrendering the Fruits of Our Actions (*Iśvarapraṇidhāna*)

Iśvarapraṇidhāna is a special kind of devotion or intention. It involves surrendering our ego while pursuing an action and offering up the results of the action to the greater good, or (for some) to the Divine. I've heard *iśvarapraṇidhāna* referred to as "excellence in action," which means that the excellence is in the doing of the action in and of itself, not solely in the results.

I know from personal experience that I want to be served by my actions! I often find myself doing something for a specific self-serving result, not necessarily for a higher purpose. *What's wrong with doing things to benefit ourselves? Why involve a higher purpose?* One reason to avoid sole ownership of our actions is to free us from negative feelings that arise when we don't get the expected results from these actions. We don't like it when things don't go our way. We feel disappointed, angry, and even cheated.

On the other hand, if we pursue an action with the goal of wholeheartedly doing the action, in of itself, we feel good, whether or not any goal was met. We can feel satisfied that we did our best, regardless of the outcome.

4.24.1 What actions have you taken recently without a strong desire for a specific result? For example, have you ridden a bike just for the pleasure of riding, rather than to burn calories or to log a certain number of miles? List one or two "result-less" actions you've taken.________________________

____

____

____

Giving to receive. All of us have had moments in which we helped someone else, with the expectation that the favor would be returned. "I'll link to your webpage, if you'll link to mine . . ." You may have also had moments in which you helped someone without the expectation of getting something in return. The practice of *iśvarapraṇidhāna* is characterized by doing actions while managing expectations about the results.

Iśvarapraṇidhāna involves our appreciation of all the knowledge that ever has been and will ever be. It is the attitude of humility that we offer toward the infinite knowledge and wisdom of the world.

As you practice Yoga, you tap into this ever-present knowledge, and even into your inner light of knowledge. That is the knowledge of all the *yamas* and *niyamas* and various qualities that move you toward a life full of peace, and, for some, enlightenment. This doesn't mean that we will fully understand this deep knowledge at every moment, for as Soren Kierkegaard reminds us:

Life can only be understood backwards; but it must be lived forwards.

PART 5

REDUCE CONFLICT TO BUILD CONNECTION

In Part 2, we identified types of *vṛtti* (activities of the mind). At any given moment, a myriad of thoughts come and go in our minds. Many are neutral thoughts that don't present any problems, such as the ones that arise when you are backing out of your driveway.... *put on seatbelt, check mirrors, clear the area, reverse*, and so on.

Discomfort comes from identifying with certain thoughts—especially negative ones or grasping ones, such as *I hate this car, I wish I made more money, I'm not successful enough.* We can try to relieve our discomfort in various ways. We might turn to nicotine or alcohol to ease our mind. We might numb ourselves with food or computer games. But these can frequently lead to more disturbance of our mind, as well as to isolation from others. We may choose to go for a run to relieve stress. Obviously, there are healthy and unhealthy ways to deal with our minds. In Part 5 I will try to deconstruct patterns of thinking that have the potential to be harmful and that can disconnect us from our *authentic* self, as well as from other people.

CHAPTER

25

Working Through the *Vṛtti-Saṁskāra* Cycle

In Part 2, *vṛtti* is defined as "activities of the mind," and in Part 3, *saṁskāras* is defined as "habits of mind." The term *vṛtti* refers to the thought that is present in our consciousness in a given moment. The term *saṁskāras*, also called "latent impressions," refers to all thoughts and experiences that we have ever had. In other words, we have an ocean of thoughts in our mind (*saṁskāras*). It is an ocean that is never still; waves (*vṛtti*) are constantly passing through the water. In western terms, we would say that *saṁskāra* refers to the unconscious mind and that awareness of a current thought refers to the conscious mind.

The complexity begins as we explore how and why certain thoughts arise in the conscious mind . . . and why some thoughts become habitual.

The *vṛtti-saṁskāra* cycle refers to recurring thought patterns so deeply instilled in our minds we don't question their validity. They may have been instilled by our family, our culture, or by our personal experiences in the world. The following flow chart illustrates this cycle.

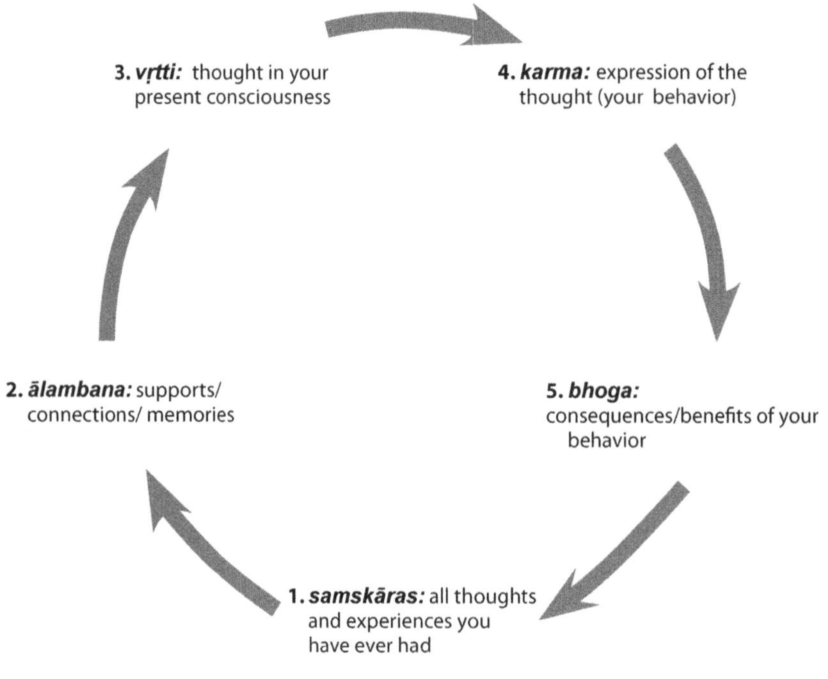

1.	***Saṁskāras***, or latent impressions, are stored in our unconscious mind.
2.	***Ālambana:*** A thought or experience triggers connection to a previous thought or experience.
3.	***Vṛtti:*** A thought arises in our present consciousness.
4.	***Karma:*** We either let the thought move along, or we engage in a behavior as a result of it.
5.	***Bhoga:*** We experience the results of our behavior. These get stored as *saṁskāras*, and the cycle repeats.

Here's an example of how this can play out:

1. I eat chocolate and find it delicious. The experience gets stored as a *saṁskāra*, or latent impression.
2. Later, someone offers me a piece of chocolate, and I immediately recall the past pleasure of eating chocolate.
3. The thought arises that I want to eat the chocolate.
4. As a result of the thought, I yield to the desire and eat the chocolate.
5. I experience a feeling of pleasure from eating the chocolate. The pleasurable feeling is then stored as a stronger, more intensified latent impression.

This cycle appears harmless, but it can lead to a compulsion or a conflict. I recall the pleasure of having eaten chocolate before. I might also have conflicting memories of having overindulged in chocolate, which produces feelings of guilt or shame. Still, I can't resist eating the chocolate, which leads to uncontrolled eating and which produces more shame. As a result, I've reinforced a strong *saṁskāra* of desire/shame in my unconscious mind that is connected to the thought of chocolate.

Saṁskāras. Our experiences can create either a conflicted *saṁskāra* or a neutral *saṁskāra*. Here's another example of an unhealthy thought cycle that creates conflict within the mind and in relationships with others.

Karen has a strong disagreement with Sarah and, as a result, Karen feels wounded. For several days afterward, Karen obsessively relives the argument and re-experiences her angry and hurt feelings. By doing this, she unknowingly nurtures a thought pattern of anger and resentment. This thought pattern becomes so deeply embedded in Karen's mind that the mere mention of Sarah's name produces a surge of anger.

Now let's explore our own examples of a negative *vṛtti-saṁskāra* cycle.

Continued on next page

5.25.1

Briefly describe an incident that provoked anger or resentment in you.

____

____

____

____

What thoughts were associated with the incident?____________________

____

____

____

What feelings were associated with the incident?____________________

____

____

____

Did you relive the incident over and over in your mind? Explain.____________________

____

____

____

How did you cope with uncomfortable feelings associated with the incident? ____________________

____

____

____

Describe any uncomfortable feelings you have as you revisit the incident today: ____________________

____

____

____

Did you resolve the incident in a way that interrupted the negative *vṛtti-saṁskāra* cycle? Explain.

____

____

____

In the previous example, not only does Karen create conflict, she breaks the connection she has with her friend Sarah. To reduce conflict, it is important to look at behaviors that stem from unhealthy thought patterns. Let's look deeper into step four: karma.

Karma is the expression of perceived thoughts—that is, our behavior. In the *vṛtti-saṁskāra* cycle, our thoughts, feelings, and memories lead to behaviors. Understanding our karma, or behavior, requires keen awareness of our emotional cycles and triggers. Such awareness, along with our ability to tolerate momentary discomfort, can save us from unhealthy *saṁskāras*.

5.25.2

List some situations that trigger in you the feelings below.

- Frustration: __________
- Anger/Resentment: __________
- Anxiety/Fear: __________
- Jealousy/Envy: __________
- Loneliness: __________
- Depression/Sadness: __________

List some of the ways you can avoid creating negative thought patterns when you have the feelings listed above. __________

By investigating our thought patterns, we can see the connection between these patterns and our repeated behaviors. This insight allows us to begin reducing conflict in our minds and our lives.

To bring more peace and happiness into our lives, we must encourage change in our minds. By recognizing unconscious compulsions, we can begin to interrupt them to bring about change. What changes would bring about more peace and happiness for us? We might want to end our critical self-talk. We might want to refrain from quickly jumping to anger in certain situations. We might want to find a solution for our sense of loneliness.

5.25.3 If you could change the way your mind operates, what changes would you make? Tell how you might make these changes.

____

____

____

Ālambana. The Sanskrit word *ālambana* means "support" or "trigger"—*support*, in the sense of advocating for our goals, and trigger, in the sense of provoking reactivity away from our goals. As presented in the *vṛtti-saṁskāra* cycle graph, a memory or other type of trigger brings an unconscious thought into the present, conscious mind.

Ālambana can either keep us in a rut or help bring about changes in our mind. For example, suppose we wanted to stop smoking. If going to a nightclub triggers our desire to smoke, we might decide to avoid going to nightclubs. In this case, we would be employing *ālambana*, in the sense of *support*, to help us break the smoking habit. Along these same lines, we could also decide to surround ourselves with people who don't smoke.

5.25.4 Let's explore our efforts to break unwanted habits and adopt desirable habits.

- What habit are you currently trying to break or would like to break?______________________

  ____

- Why do you want to break this habit?____

  ____

- What supports are (or might be) helpful to reaching your goal?______________________

  ____

  ____

- What thoughts or behaviors interfere with (or might interfere with) reaching your goal? _____

  ____

  ____

- What habit are you currently trying to adopt or would like to adopt? ______________________

  ____

- Why do you want to adopt this habit?____

  ____

- What supports might be helpful to reaching your goal?______________________

  ____

- What thoughts or behaviors might interfere with reaching your goal?______________________

  ____

  ____

Unhealthy habits can become so deeply ingrained in us that we hardly notice them. That's the power of the *vṛrti-saṁskāra* cycle. In order to change these habits and bring more peace into our life we must first recognize our thinking or behavior as unhealthy. Next, we have to desire change strongly enough to adopt a plan or practice.

Pratipakṣa bhāvana is the practice of cultivating the opposite thought or action from one you would normally choose. Let's suppose that a person has fallen prey to the thought "My partner never listens to me." That thought triggers an onslaught of negative thoughts about the partner and about the relationship.

Fortunately, this person has enough maturity and insight to understand that the thought "My partner never listens to me" may not be true. She has an awareness that dwelling on the thought is harming her relationship, so she replaces it with an opposite thought: "My partner *often* listens to me."

This leads her to more closely observe interactions with her partner. She begins to notice that the replacement thought is actually true—her partner *does* often listen to her, in many ways she failed to see, because she was often preoccupied with her *own* needs and expectations. She'd been judging her partner according to her own standard of how her partner should demonstrate listening.

5.25.5

Using *pratipakṣa bhāvana*—replacing a problematic thought or action with an opposite one—can give us insight into our habitual ways of thinking and acting. Notice in yourself any resistance to accepting the opposite thought or behavior. Here is an example of *pratipakṣa bhāvana*:

(Habitual thought) *If someone criticizes me, it's necessary to criticize that person in return.*

(Opposite thought) *If someone criticizes me, it's not necessary to criticize that person in return.*

- What habitual thought causes problems for you? Why is the thought problematic?__________

____

____

____

____

____

- State the opposite of this thought. Could this thought be true in any way? Why or why not? __

____

____

____

____

____

Practicing *pratipakṣa bhāvana* requires that we develop an "inner witness" to our thoughts. We cannot replace unhealthful thoughts with opposite, healthful ones unless we're able to observe our thoughts, rather than immediately acting on them. Doing this eventually leads to changed behaviors.

For example, a person who wants to curb a sugar habit would begin by noticing the desire for sweets and the thought that accompanies it (*I need cookies*). This person would replace that thought with an opposite thought (*I* don't *need cookies. I want them because I'm addicted to sugar, but eating it leaves me wanting more and feeling ashamed).*

One aspect of compulsions is that in the midst of them, we forget that we have choices. Identifying choices for ourselves reduces the sense that we're helpless in the face of our desires and cravings. Think of the "inner witness" as a "pause" button. Instead of helplessly operating on "play," we press "pause," regroup, consider our goals, make a different choice, and then resume "play."

Our compulsive behavior doesn't mean that there's something inherently wrong with us. It just means that we have an unhealthy *vṛtti-saṁskāra* cycle that we need to become aware of. It's a sign that we need to examine our thinking. When we look more closely at our thinking, we often discover that our actions are driven by thoughts that have little or no basis in reality. Or, we discover that the thoughts are too narrow, rigid, or critical. All of us have such thoughts. But there is no commandment that says we must obey them. You've no doubt heard the saying "Don't believe everything you think."

Transformation. Reducing conflict and building connection involves increasing awareness of our *vṛtti saṁskāra* cycles through *āsana*, *prāṇāyāma*, and meditation. To detach from our thinking and observe our thoughts requires a quiet mind. In order to quiet the mind, we need to be fully present during *āsana*, *prāṇāyāma*, and meditation. Thus, the awareness and the practice by themselves change our behaviors.

EXERCISE

5.25.6

Schedule a ten-minute (or longer) āsana practice today. In this practice, we will direct our focus solely on our movement and breath, in order to quiet our mind.

❶ With your eyes closed, flow through this sequence: child pose → hands and knees → downward-facing dog → hands and knees → child pose. Start in child pose, with the hips sitting back toward your heels, your arms extended forward, and your head down and eyes closed. Inhale and raise yourself so that you are putting equal weight in your hands and knees to form a tabletop. Exhale, flex your feet (tucking your toes under), and move your hips up and back over the heels while straightening your spine. (There is no need for the heels to be grounded or the legs to be straight). Inhale back to the tabletop position, and then exhale back to child pose.

Your mind may stray if you are unaccustomed to moving in this way. Ignore any thoughts about the "correct way" of doing this practice. This isn't about structure but about focusing on the sensation of moving your body. If your mind strays, come back to the sensation of your spine moving through this sequence. Flow through this cycle six or more times.

❷ From child pose, inhale and rise to your knees. Coming to an upright kneeling position with the arms extended upward. Then exhale, bring your arms back down, and return to child pose. As you come back down to child pose, you may want to imagine that you're releasing unhealthy *saṁskāra* cycles. Flow through this movement six or more times.

❸ Stand with your legs wider than your shoulders with your arms reaching out to the side. As you exhale, bend at the hip and extend the arms down, reaching for your toes. Bend the knees as needed. Inhaling, open the arms wide as you straighten the spine and return to the starting position. Repeat the sequence six or more times.

❹ Stand with your feet 3 or 4 inches apart and your arms at your sides. With your eyes closed, inhale while gently arching your back and lifting your arms out to the side to shoulder height. Feel your chest lifting and a change in your upper back. Exhale back to the beginning standing position, with your arms at your sides. Repeat this movement three or more times.

❺ For a minute or two, stand tall, with calm awareness of the movement of your breath and the sensation of your body at rest.

Write about your thoughts and feelings as you moved through the āsana practice.

____

____

____

____

____

____

Continued on next page

EXERCISE 5.25.6

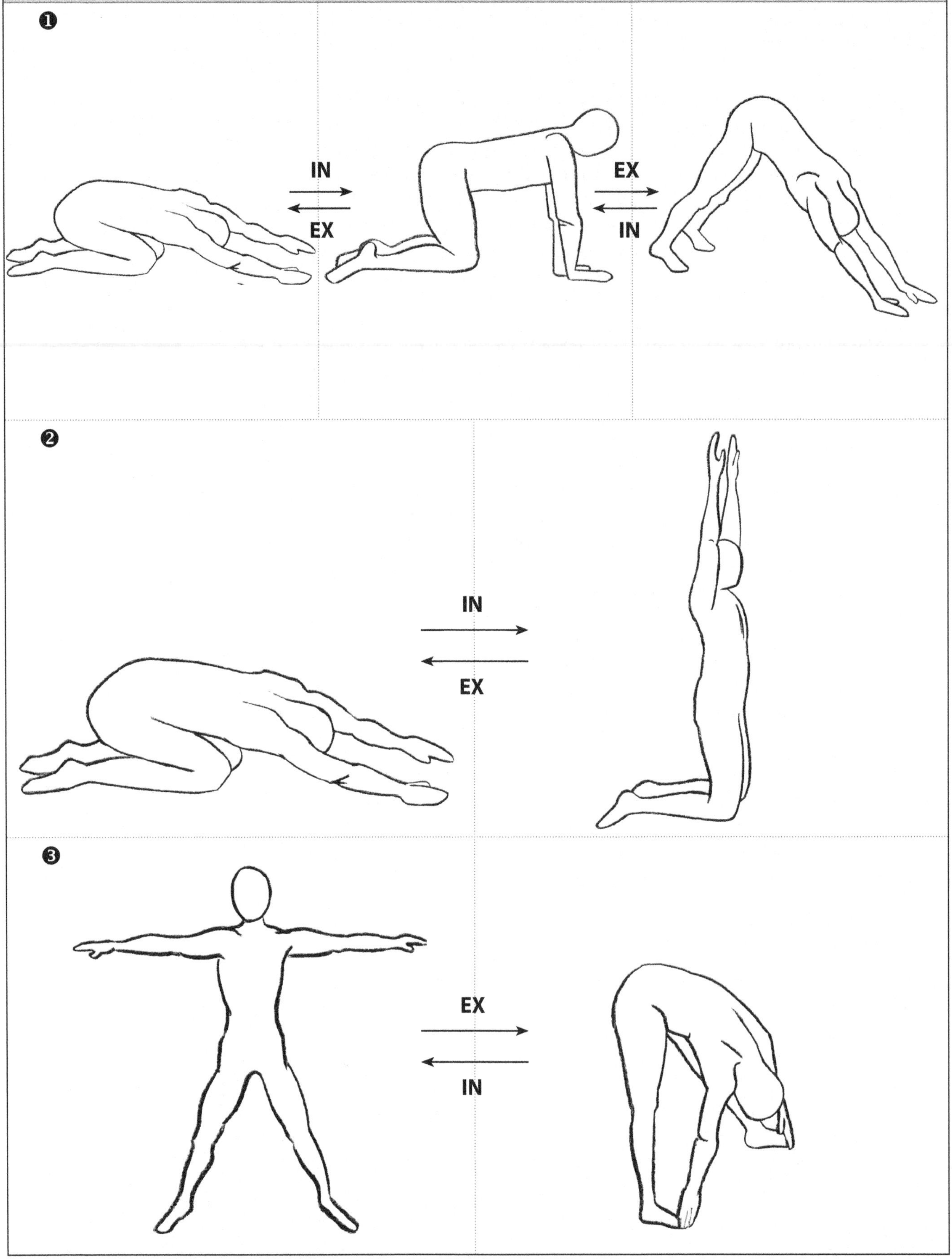

EXERCISE 5.25.6

5.25.6

❹

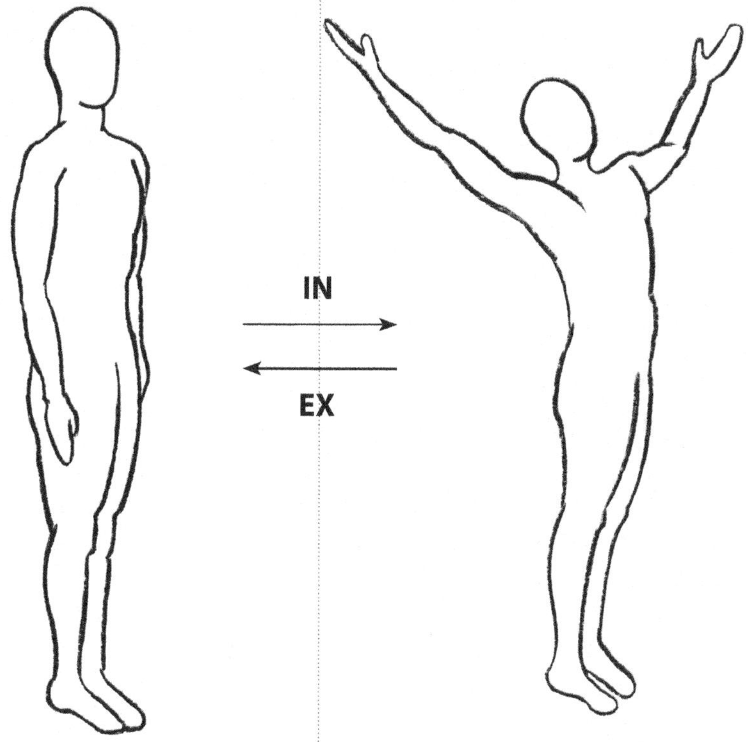

❺

Sources of *saṁskāras.* What is the source of our habitual patterns? I can identify the origin of one of my *vṛtti-saṁskāra* cycles. As a child, I was a competitive gymnast. This entailed hours of practice each week. Our coaches frequently weighed us, and we were praised for perfection of our bodies and frowned upon when there was the teeniest flaw. This push toward perfection made a deep impression on my unconscious mind because I wanted to please my coaches and parents and excel at gymnastics.

As I grew into womanhood, magazines and television reinforced this goal of bodily perfection. My developing mind deepened the impression that I didn't have value or respect unless my body was a "10."

These experiences produced an unhealthy *vṛtti-saṁskāra* cycle that created a disordered body image as well as an eating disorder. Thankfully, my Yoga practices have helped free me from my unhealthy thinking.

Do you have a similar story? We'll explore this in the next exercise.

5.25.7 Sometimes it's difficult to identify the origin of a *vṛtti-saṁskāra* cycle or pattern. Answer the following questions to the best of your ability.

- What is an unhealthy thought pattern that you developed over time? ______________________

  ____

  ____

- What is the origin of this pattern? How old were you when this pattern first developed? ______

  ____

  ____

  ____

- What role did culture, including the media, play in the development of the pattern? ________

  ____

  ____

  ____

- What role did friends, family members, teachers, coworkers, or others play in the development of the pattern?____

  ____

  ____

  ____

- To what extent, if any, does this pattern disrupt your daily life? ______________________

  ____

  ____

  ____

Creating lasting change. To create real change, we must create new thought patterns, *saṁskāras*. In order to do this, the new thought patterns must be enticing. By using *pratipakṣa bhāvana*, we create and act on opposite thoughts, but if an old pattern has a deep groove in our mind, the newly created thought pattern can easily fall off the track. Persistence is the key to meaningful, long-lasting change. This includes keeping up with our Yoga practices. These practices quiet the mind and bring us back to a desire for peace, which reinforces the newly created, healthier patterns of thinking.

Carving out time in our schedule for daily Yoga practices such as the one that follows is essential to having more peace in our life.

5.25.8

Allow 10 minutes for this practice of *prāṇāyāma*.

First, begin with a few gentle movements of your choice to prepare for *prāṇāyāma*. Then find a comfortable seated position, get in touch with your resting breath, and begin the exercise.

1. Take a free inhale and then exhale for 4 seconds. Repeat two more times.
2. Take a free inhale and then exhale for 6 seconds. Repeat two more times.
3. Take a free inhale and then exhale for 8 seconds. Repeat two more times.
4. Take a free inhale and then exhale for 6 seconds. Repeat two more times.
5. Take a free inhale and then exhale for 4 seconds. Repeat two more times.

When you have finished the exercise, write about your experience:

____

____

____

____

____

____

Daily Practices. To engage in daily Yoga practices amid other things vying for our time, you need a "feel-good" element to motivate you to return to the practices. If we see the practices as just another chore on our daily list, we'll be tempted to put them off "until tomorrow."

Your practice needs a "feel-good" sensation like what you'd get from a catnap, a great meal, or a touching conversation with a friend. For some people, the meditation aspect of Yoga is very difficult at first. It simply doesn't feel good. Sitting quietly feels almost impossible in the midst of our loud and frenzied lives. To become aware of the endless flow of our thoughts is sometimes disturbing.

But this changes with practice. Sitting quietly becomes easier and the flow of thoughts less bothersome. Eventually, a meditation practice produces feelings of calmness and wholeness.

The goal of yogic meditation is to lead us to a feeling of peace so strong that we begin to take on attributes of that pleasant sensation. For that to happen, it can be helpful to have a meditation object or mantra that we associate with a positive and peaceful feeling.

5.25.9 Think of an object, a word, or a phrase that evokes a good feeling for you. The feeling may be one of being comforted, soothed, or loved. The feeling also may have a bodily component to it, such as a warm sensation in the heart region.

Once you find an object or mantra that fits this category, set a timer for 5 minutes and begin your meditation. Try to keep your mind on the object or mantra and its associated feeling. When your mind floats away, just bring it back to the object or mantra and the feeling associated with it.

After the 5 minutes have passed, write about any thoughts and feelings you recall during this time of focus.

____

____

____

____

____

____

Transformation takes patience. We may fall in and out of our Yoga practice because of our hectic schedules. We may revert to old habits under duress. When our practice is spotty, we may still hope to achieve inner peace. But reaching this goal takes time and patience. A spotty practice cannot produce consistent results. To fulfill its promise, Yoga must be a regular, ongoing practice.

Another important point is that inner transformation is not always readily visible to the eye. I'm reminded of this interpretation of the "Tortoise and the Hare" fable: The Hare proposes a race home, and the Turtle simply retreats into his shell, for he is already home.

This concept is illuminated by the poem from Portia Nelson.

Autobiography in Five Short Chapters

I.

I walk down the street.

There is a deep hole in the sidewalk.

I fall in.

I am lost . . . I am helpless.

It isn't my fault.

It takes me forever to find a way out.

II.

I walk down the same street.

There is a deep hole in the sidewalk.

I pretend I don't see it.

I fall in again.

I can't believe I am in the same place.

But it isn't my fault.

It still takes a long time to get out.

III.

I walk down the same street.

There is a deep hole in the sidewalk.

I see it is there.

I still fall in . . . it's a habit.

My eyes are open.

I know where I am.

It is my fault.

I get out immediately.

IV.

I walk down the same street.

There is a deep hole in the sidewalk.

I walk around it.

V.

I walk down another street.

5.25.10

What words, lines, or stanzas of the poem especially appealed to you? Explain.

How is the message in the poem similar to (or different from) how you would describe your own journey?

CHAPTER

26 Putting Sūtra 1.33 into Practice

In Chapter 4 we described the *yamas* and *niyamas* as the qualities we gain from our Yoga practice. The *Yoga Sūtras* promote additional virtues that we should actively cultivate in order to have peaceful minds. These are described in line 33 of Chapter One (1.33) of the *Yoga Sūtras* as

- ***maitrī*** ("friendliness" or "friendship")
- ***karuṇā*** ("compassion")
- ***muditā*** ("joy")
- ***upekṣā*** ("non-appraising")

Those who possess these virtues have reduced conflict within and without, and have secured a connection between the outer world and their inner selves.

***Maitrī* (friendliness/friendship).** The word *maitrī* can also mean "benevolence." Recently, someone I consider unethical and malicious was given a lofty promotion. That such a person would receive this reward made me furious. In the meantime, this person had cheerfully accepted the position and was unaware of my anger. The saying mentioned in Chapter 13, "Holding hatred toward another person is like swallowing poison and expecting the other person to die," reflects my reaction. I was poisoning my own peace of mind over the other person's gain. I realized that, for my own peace of mind, I needed to apply *maitrī*, an attitude of friendliness toward the good fortune of someone else, in spite of my judgment about that person's character.

Maitrī is friendliness—not just toward others but toward ourselves, too.
Be your own best friend today, not superficially, but on a deeper level. Read the following poem by Derek Walcott and journal your reaction.

Love After Love

The time will come
when, with elation,
you will greet yourself arriving
at your own door, in your own mirror,
and each will smile at the other's welcome,
and say, sit here. Eat.
You will love again the stranger who was your self,
Give wine. Give bread. Give back your heart
to itself, to the stranger who has loved you

all your life, whom you ignored
for another, who knows you by heart.
Take down the love-letters from the bookshelf

the photographs, the desperate notes,
peel your own image from the mirror.
Sit. Feast on your life.

5.26.1

From your point of view, what is the theme, or main idea, of the poem "Love After Love"?

What do you think the poet means in the line "You will love again the stranger who was your self"?

Have you ever seemed a stranger to yourself? Explain.

What do you think interferes with giving our heart to the "stranger who has loved you all your life"?

What thoughts or feelings arose in you while reading "Love After Love"?

5.26.2

Read "Love After Love" again, slowly and attentively. Then do the following breathing exercise (a variation of pratiloma *prāṇāyāma*). Set a timer for 5 minutes.

1. Breathing through the left nostril only, inhale and exhale for 2 breaths. Refer to the image from 4.22.4 for hand placement, if needed.
2. Using *ujjayi* breathing, inhale and exhale for 2 breaths.
3. Breathing through the right nostril only, inhale and exhale for 2 breaths.
4. Return to *ujjayi* breathing for 2 breaths.

Repeat steps 1 through 4 until 5 minutes have passed.

Did you have any additional insights, feelings, or reactions to the poem after this exercise? Explain.

____

____

____

____

____

____

____

***Karuṇā* (compassion).** We have all found ourselves secretly delighting in the misfortunes of someone else. This can feel momentarily satisfying, but in the end it cultivates harshness or cruelty in our mind. The alternative to this is to practice *karuṇā*: compassion and kindness.

I have cut myself down after making mistakes. In return, I fell into a depression and withdrew from my life for a time. Now I practice *karuṇā* toward myself after making a mistake. I acknowledge that I'm still learning to be a better person and that through my mistakes I find insight into my behavior and word choices. We may feel unworthy of forgiveness, but it brings a release from the darkness to share with friends what happened and to seek help when needed.

Karuṇā also implies the desire to remove another person's suffering. We may find it easy to demonize our partners when they react with anger toward us. But in such moments, we can practice *karuṇā* by reminding ourselves, "I love my partner. This is not how they usually behave, so something must be wrong. How can I help rather than fuel their anger"?

Before taking a job in an acute-care psychiatric clinic, I was afraid and judgmental of people who I saw talking to themselves. Once I began my work at the clinic, I learned that people who suffer from schizophrenia have no control over what they see and hear in their minds. They are simply reacting to the contents of their minds. I found out that some of these people saw abusers from their past or saw and heard ghosts in their minds. This is when I stopped judging their behavior and began to have a deep sense of compassion for those with this illness. I simply put myself in their shoes and imagined how frightening it would be to have your own mind haunt you in this way.

5.26.3 Is there a person in your life that you simply don't like, for various reasons? Try moving through the following steps to cultivate *karuṇā*.

- Why do you dislike this person? ______________________________

____

____

____

- Try to put yourself in this person's shoes. What do you think it would be like to be him or her?

____

____

____

- What might help you remove this person as a "problem" in your mind? What could help you see them as a fellow human being with all the strengths and flaws of humans? ______________

____

____

____

***Muditā* (joy).** *Muditā* refers to a gladness of heart rather than ecstatic joy. Cultivating *muditā* involves opening the heart, which is both a requirement for peace of mind and the product of peace of mind. This joy comes from enlarging our perspective—that is, from seeing beyond our own needs and wants. When we do this, our cramped, narrow ways of seeing the world begin to expand, and we connect with a more fundamental joy. We find gladness no matter what we're doing—eating a meal alone, working with others, fixing a leaky toilet, or feeding the homeless. This joyful attitude affects (infects!) others.

We often overlook the wonder of this world. Just this morning while cleaning and listening to the news, I found myself becoming grumpy. Then out of the corner of my eye I saw a large red fuzzy movement through the window. I paused, looked out, and there was the most beautiful fox. He was sitting quietly, head up, nose in the air. What an amazing sight, and so close! The experience led to a lightness and brightness in me. That is *muditā*.

There are many ways to connect with the *muditā* within you. If you are a nature lover, being in nature is one way. If you are a cyclist, a nice ride will do the trick. Through the practice of Yoga (and, in particular, meditation, which helps us gradually open to the miracle that is our life), we can learn to connect with *muditā*. Meditation leads us to a trusting acceptance of all that is. And when we can accept the reality of our life—pleasure, pain, struggles, ease, rewards, roadblocks, abundance, scarcity—we can more easily attain *muditā*. This gladness doesn't depend on everything going our way; it emerges from making peace with our lives as they are, in each moment.

5.26.4

What are some examples of *muditā* moments in your life? ______________________

____

____

____

What internal conditions allow you to more easily experience the gladness of *muditā*? ______________________

____

____

What external conditions allow you to more easily experience *muditā*? ______________________

____

____

What sometimes prevents you from experiencing *muditā*? ______________________

____

____

What changes might make it easier to experience *muditā* in your life ? ______________________

____

____

____

***Upekṣā* (non-apprasing).** Here's an example of the type of equanimity that *upekṣā* aims toward: it is the evenness of mind that lets you remain untroubled and still while a bee buzzes around you. *Sūtra* 1.33 suggests that we cultivate the same attitude in the presence of people we judge to be irritating, upsetting, or otherwise annoying. The respected commentator of the *Yoga Sūtras* Hariharananda Aranya defines *upekṣā* as "not a positive thinking, but restraining the mind from dwelling on the frailties of others."

To achieve greater equanimity, we learn to discard our usual categories: I like this/I don't like that; this is good/that is bad; I'm for this/I'm against that. It involves moving beyond our prejudices and becoming more honest with ourselves, as well as more open and available to others. *Upekṣā* doesn't mean that we ignore improper actions; it means that we act with a clear mind in order to promote peace in the world.

5.26.5

The dictionary definition of *equanimity* is "evenness of mind, especially under stress." It's easy to be calm and even-minded when we're not threatened or otherwise under stress. *Upekṣā* refers to a non-value judgment in all situations.

- What are three examples of situations in which you usually feel (or have felt) uneasy, nervous, or otherwise out of balance?

- Why is (or was) each situation troubling for you?

- For each situation, imagine that you have attained the state of *upekṣā.* Describe how you would then look and behave in each situation.

***Kṣāma* (patience).** The Sanskrit term *kṣāma* means "to have patience and tolerance with everyone." *Kṣāma* is part of the word *upekṣā*. I have included the discipline of *kṣāma* here because of its close connection to the other virtues presented in this chapter. We have all found ourselves at times disturbed by others' behavior or points of view. Sometimes we observe others' way of doing things and are seized with the impulse to offer a "better" way. *Kṣāma* begins with the recognition that we all walk on separate paths. Our practice is to allow others to build their own character and to focus our attention on building our own.

Kṣāma includes patience toward ourselves. We're trained by our culture to expect instant results, but we know from experience that real transformation is a long, slow process. It requires patience—especially patience with our eagerness to grow and develop quickly.

One of the best ways to cultivate patience is through meditation. In daily meditation, we learn just how impatient we are. We also learn to tolerate our energetic thoughts and impulses without acting on them.

5.26.6

Describe a recent situation in which you were impatient. What thoughts and feelings were associated with this experience? ________________________________

____

____

____

If you drew a picture of your impatience, what would the drawing show? ________________________________

____

____

____

What are your usual strategies for managing impatience? ________________________________

____

____

____

Describe a situation in which you showed true patience, as opposed to grit-your-teeth tolerance.

____

____

____

The virtues presented in Sūtra 1.33 help us move toward peace of mind and away from the following:

krodha (anger)
lobha (greed)
moha (confusion)
viṣāda (sorrowful)
mātsarya (jealousy)
apāmana (feeling of insult)
asūyā (disparaging others)

5.26.7

For each undesirable quality listed below, "prescribe" as an antidote one or more of the desirable qualities addressed in this chapter: *maitrī, karuṇā, muditā,* or *upekṣā.*

- ***krodha*** (anger): ____________________
- ***lobha*** (greed): ____________________
- ***moha*** (confusion): ____________________
- ***viṣāda*** (regret): ____________________
- ***mātsarya***(jealousy): ____________________
- ***apāmana*** (feeling of insult): ____________________
- ***asūyā*** (disparaging others): ____________________

CHAPTER

27

Finding Peace Wherever You Are

Yoga *Sūtra* 1.20 reads sraddha virya *smṛti samadhi prajna purvaka itaresam.* This sūtra refers to cultivating the faith that we are on the right path as Yoga practitioners. The peaceful feeling generated by our practice supports us like a loving mother or father.

Throughout our day, we actively recall the peaceful, relaxed state produced by our practice. This recollection might, for example, result in a smile. The smile then evokes warm, peaceful feelings that ease tension in our body. With time, the smile becomes so associated with a peaceful feeling that we can use it during a walk, or while sitting in nature, to reinforce our peaceful mind with a sense of appreciation for all life, especially our own.

In this way, it is easy to see that Yoga can be done anywhere, at any time. A Yoga room is not necessary.

EXERCISE 5.27.1

5.27.1 Here's a Yoga practice that can be done in your kitchen, using the countertop and a chair. You can do the movements for as many repetitions as you like.

Countertop

❶ Place your hands on the countertop. Inhale and rise up onto your toes, while using the countertop for balance as needed.

❷ Remaining on your toes, exhale while bending your knees into a gentle squat.

❸ Inhale as you straighten your knees. Then exhale, as you lower your heels to the floor.

Kitchen Chair

❶ Sitting tall in a chair, inhale and then exhale as you twist to the right. Inhale and return to center, continuing to sit tall. Then exhale as you twist to the left. Inhale and return to center. Repeat these side-to-side twists with the breath. You can choose to move dynamically or hold the twist for a breath or two.

❷ From a seated position, lift your right foot and place your right ankle over the left knee. Bend forward slightly and feel the stretch in your right hip and leg. Hold for six breaths. Release, and repeat the stretch with the opposite foot.

❸ Sit tall, with both feet on the floor, hands resting on your thighs. Inhale and raise your arms from the front while slightly arching your back and lifting your chin. Feel the stretch in your chest and the arch in your spine. Then exhale your arms back to your lap or your sides and straighten your back.

EXERCISE 5.27.1

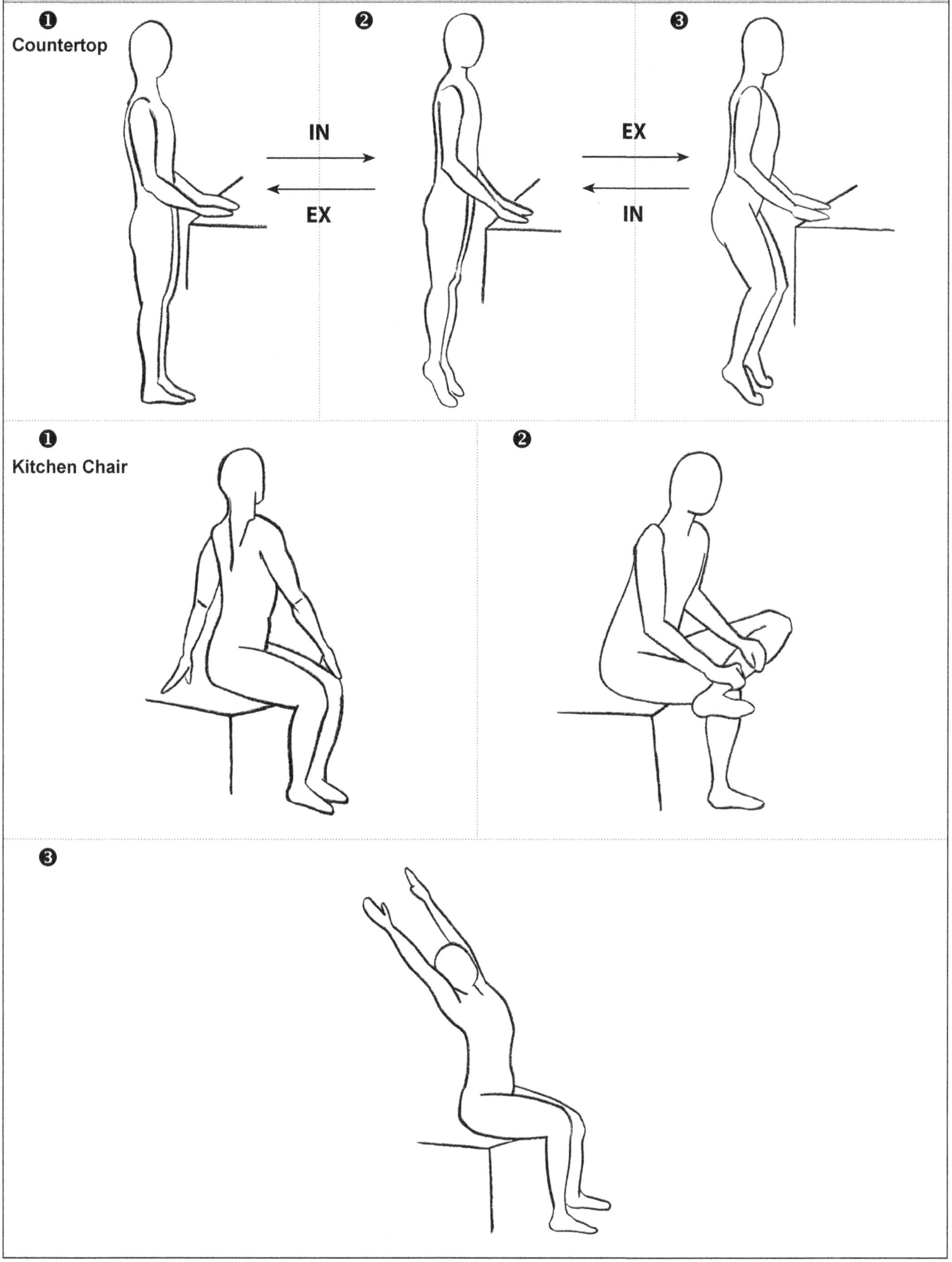

5.27.2

At any time during your day, you can encourage a peaceful feeling by practicing the following paced breathing for a few moments.

1. Take a resting position, either seated or lying down.
2. For one or two minutes, simply breathe freely and quietly.
3. When you feel ready, begin lengthening your inhale and exhale. Start with a 3-second count for your inhale and a 3-second count for your exhale.
4. Add 1 second to the next inhale and 1 second to the next exhale.
5. Continue to add seconds to the breath cycles, staying within your comfort zone.
6. When you feel that you're pushing the limits of your comfort, return to normal, comfortable breathing.

Note any thoughts and feelings that arise with this practice:______________________________

Walking *āsana* practice. *Āsana* is necessary for a healthy body, which aids in developing a healthy mind. But *āsana* is not exercise. *Āsana* is staying present with your movements as you lead them with your breath. The focus is consistently drawn inward, rather than to external sounds and sensations. When you're not doing *āsana* but simply stretching and exercising, you can converse with a friend, listen to music, watch television, and so on without degrading the stretching and exercise. But *āsana* requires steady, mindful focus. This does not mean that exercise is less beneficial than Yoga! Cardiovascular exercise is highly effective for anxiety, depression, and general health. But that is a topic for another book. For now, let's experience the kind of focused mindfulness that we use in a Yoga practice.

5.27.3

Set aside time for a ten- to fifteen-minute walk, preferably in a setting that has natural features such as trees, grass, flowers, or a body of water. For this walk, leave your phone behind (or turn it off) as well as any other electronic devices. Proceed at a pace in which you can comfortably inhale for three steps and exhale for three steps. Follow one or more of these mindfulness exercises as you walk:

1. Focus on sensations in each foot as it contacts the earth. Notice the movement of your ankle, heel, ball of the foot, and toes.
2. Notice sensations in your lower leg, knee, and upper leg.
3. Notice sensations in your hips, torso, neck, arms, hands, and head.
4. "Inhale" the sights, sounds, and smells during your walk.

After your walk, jot down notes about your thoughts, feelings, and bodily sensations during the walk.

In Part 5 we've learned how certain principles and attitudes can help build connection within us, with our community, and with the world. We've learned to take heed of the *vṛtti-saṁskāra* cycle that pervades our mind. With this awareness, we are able to press the "pause" button on our learned-response system and make choices that lead to more peace in our lives.

Along with that, we explored Yogic attitudes that help us more effectively and deeply engage with others. These everyday concepts are pathways to an abiding sense of peace. They teach us how to touch the world more authentically. They provide us with the tools to heed the call of Mahatma Gandhi and "Be the change that you wish to see in the world."

CONCLUSION

We've explored many aspects of Yoga in this workbook. We began with the translation of the word *vṛtti*, as "profession," in the sense that the mind's job is to produce thoughts. In the early exercises, we practiced being aware of our thoughts without judging them. Subsequently, we narrowed our focus to types of thought: correct and incorrect knowledge, imagination, deep sleep, and memory. Understanding these thought types is a step toward the goal of moving *viparyaya* (incorrect understanding) to *pramāna* (correct understanding).

From there we looked into what Yoga calls our "root afflictions"—the *kleśas*: illusion, overidentification, attachment, aversion, and fear (called *avidyā*, *asmitā*, *rāga*, *dveṣa*, and *abhiniveśa*). The *kleśas* are necessary for our existence, but when unchecked they can deter us from peace. Keeping them in check requires reflection on the *yamas* and *niyamas*: attitudes and behaviors that help clarity of mind.

Finally, we delved into the cyclical working of the mind (the *vṛtti-saṁskāra* cycle). We examined the arising of thoughts into our consciousness and the action or inaction we take regarding them. We looked at how, when we slow down and practice awareness, our unconscious reactivity is reduced and we experience a sense of freedom and empowerment.

Finding peace of mind in the midst of everyday life in our chaotic world is a lifelong practice. You may want to continue practicing the exercises in this workbook long after your first experience of the book. You may also want to develop a home practice of Yoga. If so, I strongly recommend that you undertake the practice with an experienced teacher. In the meantime, here are some ideas to get you started. These are not strict rules, just helpful suggestions.

1. In your Yoga practice, try to always include *āsana*, *prāṇāyāma*, and meditation, in that order. It is hard to sit still without first having done some movement, and it is hard to focus and concentrate without having first taken some deep breaths to clear your mind of the day's "residue."

2. In *āsana*, it is nice to begin with standing postures and then move toward floor postures. If you prefer, you can do a practice that involves only seated or supine movements. Try to include movement of the spine in all four directions (forward, backward, side bending, twisting).

3. With *prāṇāyāma*, never overly challenge yourself. Even when you are testing your ability to lengthen and deepen the breath, or to hold the breath, stay within your safety zone. Remember that your breath is directly linked to your mental state. Since the goal is to move toward meditation, you will want to keep your mind free of anxiety or frustration.

4. When meditating, always sit comfortably, with your spine tall. Whether you are sitting in a chair or on the floor, use adequate cushioning to help you find ease in your position.

On the next few pages, I have included two generalized practices. Note that these practices do not take injuries or illnesses into account. One practice is focused on mobility, and the other is an evening practice to aid in transitioning to bedtime. Again, I strongly recommend that you work with a teacher to develop the most effective practice for you. I hope the practices I provide can give you a sense of what a healthy Yoga practice looks like.

PRACTICE 1

A practice for muscle and joint mobility • PRACTICE 1

This first practice is for mobility in the muscles and joints employs a *prāṇāyāma* practice for mental focus.

❶ Standing attentively, inhale and raise your arms from the sides and up as high as possible. Extend the shoulder and elbow joints for an extra stretch. Exhale and lower your arms back to your sides. Repeat two more times, noticing any tightness in the shoulders or arms.

❷ From a standing position, inhale and raise your arms in front of you, reaching as high as possible. Exhale, bend your knees, and sit into an imaginary chair, as if you were doing a squat, while lowering your arms to chest level. Inhale and raise your arms, as you return to standing tall. Keeping your arms raised, exhale and squat again. Focus on the sensations in your knees and hips with the up and down motion. Perform this posture several times until you feel ready to lower your arms and return to the standing position, with arms at your sides.

❸ From a standing position, inhale while lifting your heels off the ground and raising your arms out to the side. Exhale and twist your torso to the right while using your arms to aid in balancing. Inhale and return to center. Exhale and lower your heels to the ground and your arms to your sides. Perform the same sequence, this time twisting to the left. Do this *āsana* three times in each direction. Focus on keeping your feet stable and maintaining your balance. This is an advanced posture, so modify it as needed for comfort and safety.

❹ Beginning in child pose, inhale and come to your hands and knees while accentuating the concave dip in your spine. As you exhale, round your spine, creating a convex curve while you return to child pose. Do this several times, focusing on mobility in the spine.

A practice for muscle and joint mobility • PRACTICE 1

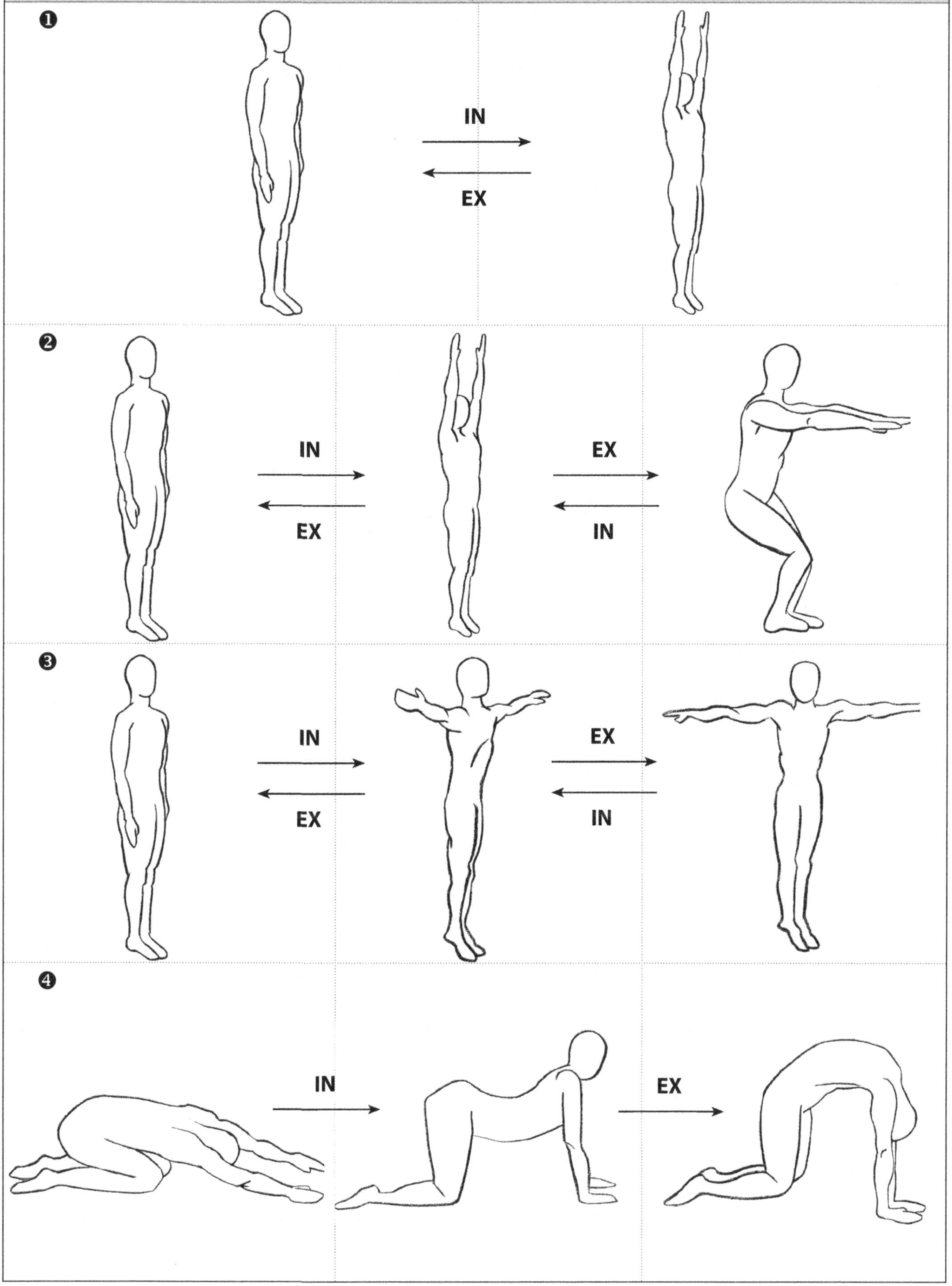

PRACTICE 1

A practice for muscle and joint mobility • PRACTICE 1

❺ Lie on your back with your knees drawn into your chest and your arms resting on the floor by your sides. Press your lower back to the ground. While maintaining that connection, lift your legs so that they make a 90-degree angle. (Don't worry if your legs do not straighten completely.) Exhale and return to the starting position. Perform these three to six times, focusing on the deep bend in your knees as they're pressed to your chest as well as the stretch in the back of your legs when they're raised.

❻ Lie on your back with your knees bent and your feet on the floor. Cross your right ankle over your left thigh. (There's no exact spot on the thigh in which the ankle must be placed; the placement depends on the position that's comfortable for you.) Inhale and lift your hips and spine, feeling an opening sensation in your right hip. Exhale and return to the starting position. Repeat on this side two more times. Then practice three times with the left ankle placed over the right thigh. Discontinue this posture if you feel cramping in your hamstrings.

❼ In a seated position on the floor, place the soles of your feet together near your pelvis. (If this is difficult, just place your feet as close together and as near your pelvis as possible. Don't force the posture.) This posture is commonly known as "butterfly position." Try to maintain a tall, straight spine, while using your leg muscles to press your knees toward the floor. Feel the sensations in your hips and spine. Maintain this position for six breaths.

❽ Now sit comfortably for *prāṇāyāma*. Use *viloma* as discussed in exercise 1.4.2 but add a counting measure. With each inhale (alternate nostril) count ten seconds. Pause and hold the breath for a moment. Then extend the exhale (*ujjayi*) for fifteen seconds. Practice the breathing for 12–24 breaths, or up to 5 minutes. Feel free to adjust the count as needed, but try to extend the exhale one-and-a-half times longer than the inhale.

At this point you may choose to begin a meditation practice or continue to sit and enjoy the feeling that *prāṇāyāma* creates.

A practice for muscle and joint mobility • PRACTICE 1

❺

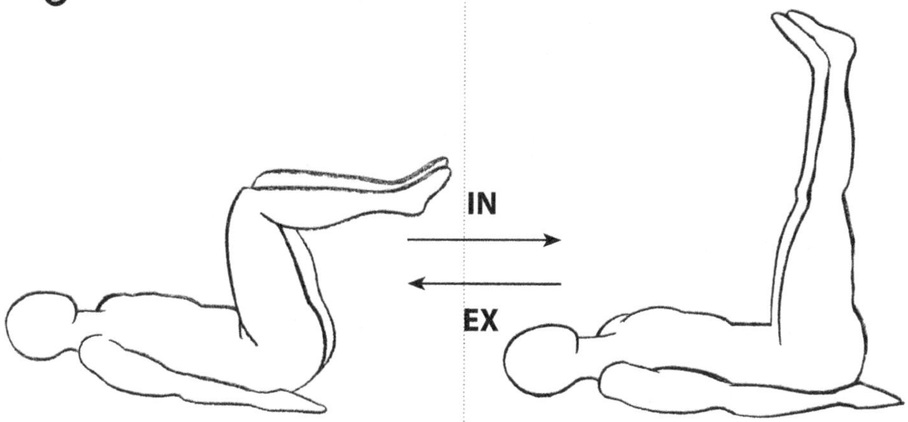

❻

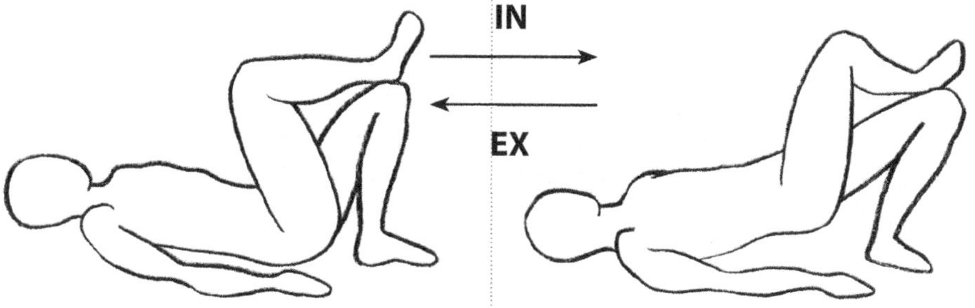

❼

❽

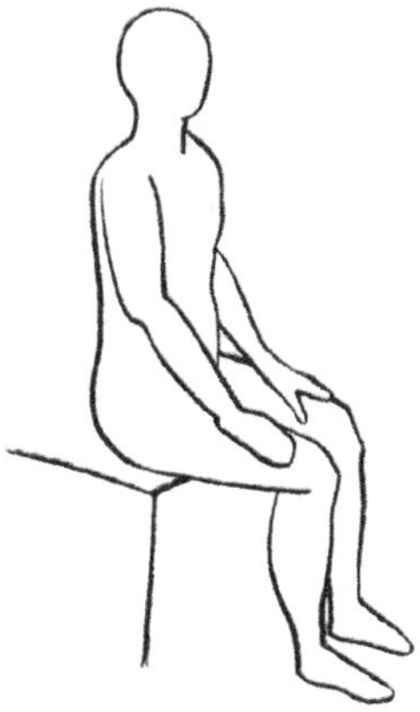

PRACTICE 2

A practice for transitioning to sleep • PRACTICE 2

This second practice aims at transitioning your body and mind from an active place to a settled state of being, and employs a *prāṇāyāma* practice to induce relaxation.

❶ Standing alert yet relaxed, inhale and raise your arms from the front. Begin exhaling slowly, drawing your abdomen in and upward. After a second or two, slowly bend your body forward and extend your fingertips forward and then down toward your toes. Finish the movement just before the exhale ends. Hold the exhale and the posture for a count of 3–5 seconds. Then begin inhaling slowly. After a second or two, begin raising your arms and then your torso all the way up to a standing position, with your arms extended toward the ceiling, as you continue to inhale. Repeat this forward bend with the breath work two more times. Then come to a relaxed standing position with your arms at your sides. Notice the challenge that holding the exhale creates. (If this becomes too difficult, hold the exhale for fewer seconds. This should not be an endurance feat!)

❷ With your arms outstretched from the sides, balance on one leg, keeping your torso straight and strong. Then hinge forward at the hip to appear like a letter "T". This posture is commonly known as "airplane position" or "warrior three." This is an advanced posture, so modify it as needed for comfort and safety. A good goal would be to hold the posture for six breaths on each leg.

❸ Come to child pose. Completely exhale and then inhale to rise into an upright kneeling posture, in which the arms are reaching upward. Exhale and fold back into child pose, holding the exhale and holding the posture for 3–5 seconds. Repeat this sequence two more times while paying close attention to your breath.

❹ Move to a position on your hands and knees, keeping a neutral spine. Exhale into the downward facing dog posture. Hold the posture and exhale for 3–5 seconds. Then inhale and return to your hands and knees. Repeat this posture two more times.

A practice for transitioning to sleep • PRACTICE 2

PRACTICE 2

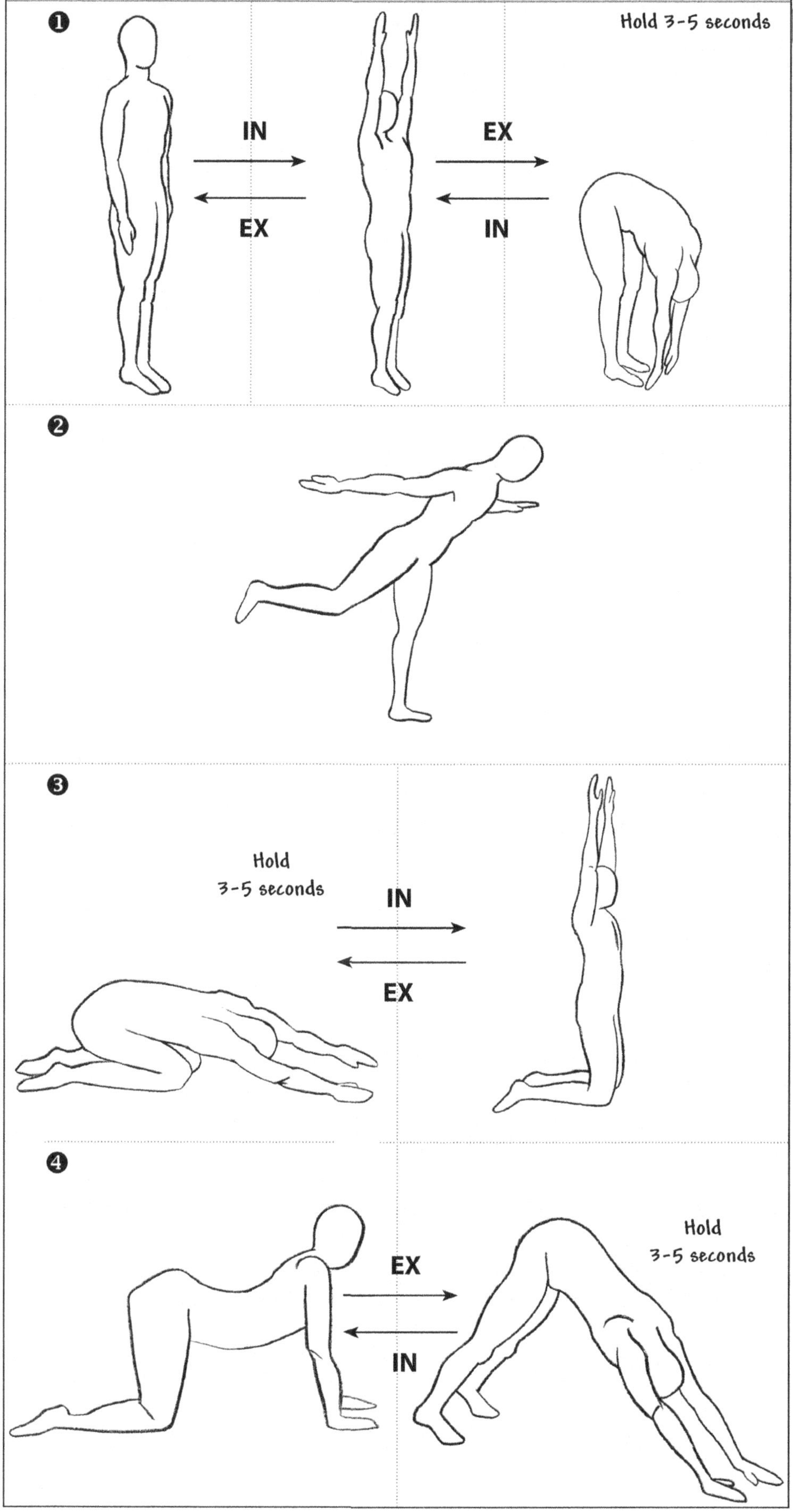

PRACTICE 2

A practice for transitioning to sleep • PRACTICE 2

❺ Lie on your back and extend your arms out from your sides. Bring your knees to your chest and then, keeping the knees bent, twist your knees to the right. For a deeper twist, bring your knees closer to your torso and right arm. For an easier twist, unfold your knees a little. Once you find yourself in a somewhat comfortable twist of the spine, hold the posture for six breaths. Then return to center and rotate your knees to the left, holding for six breaths.

❻ Continue to lie down and press your lower back to the floor. While maintaining that connection, lift your legs to make a 90-degree angle. (If your hamstring muscles are tight, your legs may not straighten completely. That's okay.) Hold the posture for six breaths. Feel your abdomen being strengthened to maintain the position.

❼ Lying on your back, draw your knees toward your chest and place your hands on your knees. Then use your hands to gently and slowly push your knees away from your chest. Draw the knees in and out with your breath. Repeat two more times. With eyes closed, be aware of your thoughts and bodily sensations as you repeat the movements.

❽ You will need a chair, wall, side of a bed, or other surface for this posture. Lie on your back and place your legs on a surface so that they are at about a 45-degree angle. When your breath feels relaxed, begin to extend your exhale mindfully. You may do this with or without counting. The important aspect of this step is the subtle quality of attention to your exhale. Extend the breath slowly to 75 percent of your maximum length. Try to repeat the same length for 10–12 breaths. Then continue inhaling and exhaling until you feel ready to continue your nightly routine and enter sleep.

PRACTICE 2

A practice for transitioning to sleep • PRACTICE 2

❺

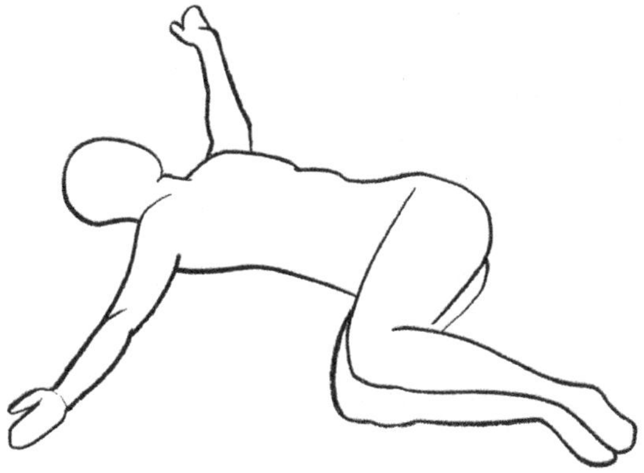

❻

❼

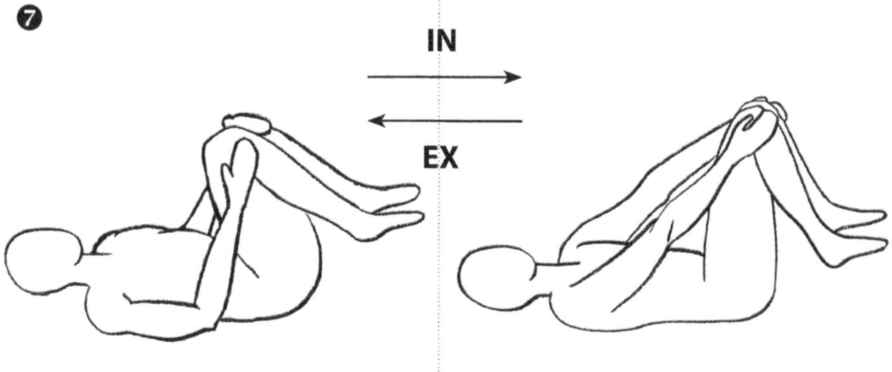

❽

For further sample practices, I recommend:

Yoga for Body, Breath, and Mind:
A Guide to Personal Reintegration, by A.G. Mohan

Yoga Therapy:
A Guide to the Therapeutic Use of Yoga and Ayurveda for Health and Fitness, by A.G. Mohan and Indra Mohan

Learning Through Yoga, by Raghu Ananthanarayanan

Thank you for your time in practicing with this workbook. I hope the information and exercises help you better understand aspects of your mind—and show the value of practicing Yoga to gain more ease in your everyday life.

Peace be with you,

Caroline

Glossary

abhiniveśa (ahb•heeny•VESH•uh) fear

ahimsā (uh•HEEM•SUH) refraining from harm

ālambana (AH•luhm•BAHN•uh) support, connections, trigger

aṅga (ON•guh) limbs

apamāna (ah•pah•MAHN•uh) feeling of insult

aparigraha (ah•par•EE•gruh•huh) non-covetousness

āsana (AHSS•uh•nuh) movements of the body or, posture

asmitā (oss•mee•TAH) "I am-ness," overidentification with the intellect and the body

asteya (uh•STAY•uh) non-stealing

asūyā (uh•soo•YUH) disparaging others

avidyā (uh•vee•D'YUH) illusion

bhāvana (b'HAH•vuh•nuh) cultivation

bhoga (b'HOE•guh) the experience of the results of behavior

brahmacarya (brah•muh•CHAR•yuh) respecting our senses

citta (chit•tuh) our conscious mind

dveṣa (d'VESH•uh) aversion to pain

iśvarapraṇidhāna (EESH•vah•ruh•prawny•DAH•nuh) surrendering the fruits of our actions

japa (JAHP•puh) to repeat, as in mantra japa

karma (CAR•muh) to do or not to do

karuṇā (car•OO•nuh) compassion

kleśa (CLAY•shuh) affliction, divided into five types

kriyā (kree•YUH) action, as in kriyā yoga, the "yoga of action"

krodha (crow•duh) anger

kṣāma (k'SHAW•muh) patience

lobha (LOBE•huh) greed

maitrī (my•tree) friendliness, friendship, or benevolence

mantra (MAHN•tra) a word or phrase to be spoken or chanted to literally "protect the mind" from unwanted and unhelpful thoughts

mātsarya (MAT•t'sar•yuh) jealousy

mejayatva (MAY•jah•yaht•vuh) trembling

moha (moe•huh) confusion

muditā (moo•dee•TAH) joy

nāḍīśodhana (nah•DEE•show•dah•nuh) a type of breath regulation by inhaling and exhaling through alternate nostrils

nidrā (nee•DRAH) deep sleep, or knowledge of sleep

nirodha (nee•ROAD•d'hah) to direct, or restrain

niyamas (nee•yaw•muss) personal attitudes gained from practice

pramāna (pruh•MAHN•nuh) correct understanding that does not change

prāṇāyāma (prah•NAH•YAH•muh) awareness and regulation of the breath

pratiloma (prah•tee•LOE•muh) a type of breath regulation in which one alternates between ujjayi breathing and alternate nostril breathing

pratipakṣa bhāvana (prah•tee•POCK•shuh buh•HAHV•uh•nuh) cultivating the opposite thought or action

rāga (RAH•guh) attachment to pleasure

saṁskāra (sahm•skar•ruh) habits of the mind, latent impressions, t houghts in the unconscious mind

śanti (SHAHN•tee) peace

santoṣa (san•TOE•shuh) contentment

satya (SAHT•yuh) truthfulness

śauca (SHAOW•cha) cleanliness

smṛti (SMRIT•tee) memory

svādhyāya (svah•d'yah•yah) studies or practices moving one nearer to their "higher" self

tapas (TOP•us) self-discipline

uḍḍīyāna-bandha (ooh•DEE•yawn•nuh BOND•duh) an inner muscular engagement of the abdominal wall while holding the exhale out after a complete breath

ujjayi (ooh•JAH•ee) a type of breath regulation in which the epiglottis and vocal folds are engaged to narrow the passageway of air through the throat

upekṣā (ooh•peck•SHUH) non-appraising, or equanimity

vikalpa (vee•call•puh) imagination

viloma (vee•LOE•muh) a type of breath regulation in which one inhales though alternate nostrils and uses the ujjayi technique to exhale

viparyaya (vee•par•yah•yah) incorrect understanding that changes with time

viṣāda (vee•SHAW•duh) sorrowful

vṛtti (VRIT•tee) thoughts/activities of the mind, a profession, a thought in the present consciousness

yamas (YAHM•muss) relational attitudes gained from practice

yoga (YO•guh) a technique/system intended for peace of mind

yoga sūtras (YO•guh SOO•truss) a primary text of Yoga providing a specific method for its path

PERMISSIONS AND CREDITS

Page 0121: *There's A Hole in My Sidewalk: The Romance of Self-Discovery*, by Portia Nelson. Copyright© 1993 by Portia Nelson. Reproduced with kind permission from Beyond Words Publishing, Hillsboro, Oregon.

Page 124: *"Love After Love" from The Poetry of Derek Walcott: 1948-2013*, selected by Glyn Maxwell. Copyright © 2014 by Derek Walcott. Reproduced with kind permission from Farrar, Straus, and Giroux.

Made in the USA
Coppell, TX
04 October 2022

84085156R00090